PLANT B

DIET

Discover 101+ Delicious Foods Scientifically Proven to Prevent Diseases. The Only Painless 21-Day Meal Plan Method That Over 127 Doctors Adopted To Improve Their Families' Health.

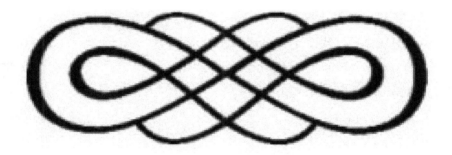

BY

Yaritza Glass

Table of Contents

INTRODUCTION

An Introduction to Plant Based Diet

What is plant based diet?

A plant based diet is a diet that involves consuming mostly or only on foods that come from plants. People understand and use the term plant based diet in different ways.

Some people interpret it as a vegan diet, which involves avoiding all animal products.

For others, a plant based diet means that plant foods, such as fruits, vegetables, whole grains, nuts, and legumes, are the main focus of their diet, but they may, occasionally, consume meat, fish, or dairy products.

A plant based diet also focuses on healthful whole foods, rather than processed foods.

Yes, it is technically a vegan diet, but there's a difference between being vegan and eating a plant-based diet for health. The decision to be vegan stems from an individual's compassion towards the lives of animals and the environment, and excludes all animal products in order to minimize harm and suffering. Vegans eat a 100% plant-based diet, but not necessarily one that is based on whole, unprocessed foods. This is where the distinction lies. The fundamental principle of a healthy (or "whole foods") plant-based diet is to promote health, and to reduce one's risk of lifestyle-related disease. In addition to excluding animal products, it also excludes processed vegan items such as vegetable oils, refined carbohydrates, and foods high in refined sugar and salt.

A diet based on whole plant foods has been shown to reduce the risk of lifestyle-related diseases, including type-2 Diabetes, heart disease, hypertension, and even certain types of cancer. New research also indicates that plant-based diets could be helpful in preventing Alzheimer's, Multiple Sclerosis, and a whole host of other degenerative diseases. What's more, eating minimally processed plant-foods greatly benefits our planet and the environment; not to mention the non-human species that inhabit it.

CHAPTER ONE

THE BENEFITS OF PLANT BASED DIET

Animal foods are also more processed than even some of the more processed plant-based choices people avoid at the store. Considering that animals are living creatures just like you and me, it makes no sense for us to spend our money on an industry that causes them suffering, destroys the environment, and causes us health problems. As rates of cancer and diabetes increase, one has to wonder if this has to do with the animal production being higher than ever and fast food restaurants serving up more animal foods that are cheaper per meal than whole, plant-based meal offerings. Though you and I can't change this overnight, we can change our health by eating a plant-based diet. I'm under the belief that if more people chose the vegan route, they'd not only feel better, but animal production demand would significantly decrease.

A plant-based diet is more economical, especially if you eat in-season and eat local produce. Check out some of these health benefits of going getting plant-powered, and start eating more plants this week. By filling your plate up with the good stuff, there's less room for the acidic animal foods that leave you sluggish and tired.

Plant-based diet doesn't have to be 100% plants or vegan, but it can be if you wish. The goal is for a majority of the foods you are eating to come from plants. These foods include bright, colorful fruits and vegetables. But they can also include other foods, such as spices, herbs and seasonings, nuts and seeds, whole grains, beans, and legumes.

It's important to think about a variety of colorful fruits and vegetables because each contains different phytonutrients to support your overall health and support your immune system. When possible, it is also good to select locally-grown, in-season foods and sometimes organically grown produce to get the most nutrient-rich foods while reducing your exposure to chemicals and pesticides.

Health benefits of eating a plant-based diet

The idea of eating "plant-based" sounds healthy. And it is. "Plant-based" is also a buzzword we're seeing more and more. But what exactly is a plant-based diet and what makes it healthy?

A plant-based diet means eating more whole foods and plants-fruits, vegetables, whole grains, legumes, and nuts and seeds. One of the best parts about eating a plant-based diet is that you can define your strictness. It doesn't necessarily mean plants only. For some, a plant-based diet does exclude all animal products (a vegan diet). For others, it's just about proportion-choosing more of your foods from plant sources than from animal sources. It's a nice way to make plants a main part of your diet without needing to completely eliminate dairy, eggs, meat and fish (you can just eat less of these).

Better nutrition

Plants are healthy-you know this-and most of us don't eat the recommended amount of fruits and veggies, so making the majority of your diet plant-based will up your produce ante, which is a nutritious choice. Fruits and vegetables are rich in vitamins, minerals, antioxidants and fiber. Fiber is a nutrient that most of us don't get enough of, and it has tons of healthy perks–it's good for your waistline, your heart, your gut and your blood sugar (read more about the amazing benefits of fiber). But, also, science shows that people's overall nutrition is usually better when they follow a vegetarian or vegan diet versus when they eat an omnivorous diet.

Weight loss

People who follow a plant-based diet tend to have lower body mass indexes (BMIs) compared to their omnivore counterparts. And research shows that people who use a vegetarian diet to lose weight are more successful not only at dropping pounds, but also at keeping them off. (See more science-backed tips for weight-loss.)

Healthier hearts

Eating a vegetarian diet may lower your risk of cardiovascular disease, and may improve other risk factors for heart disease by lowering your blood pressure and cholesterol, and improving your blood sugar control. Eating plant-based can also help quell inflammation, which raises your risk of heart disease by promoting plaque buildup in your arteries.

Lower diabetes risk

Regardless of your BMI, eating a vegetarian diet or a vegan diet lowers your risk of diabetes. In fact, one study shows that meat eaters have double the risk of diabetes compared to lacto-ovo vegetarians and vegans. Another study, this one published in February 2019, shows that people who eat a plant-based diet have higher insulin sensitivity, which is important for maintaining healthy blood sugar levels.

Cut cancer risk

Research consistently shows that regularly eating plenty of fruits, veggies, legumes and grains-aka plants-is associated with a lower cancer risk. Plus, those disease-fighting phytochemicals in plants have also been shown to prevent and thwart cancer. And, don't forget, studies also show an association between eating red and processed meats and increased cancer risk, especially colorectal cancer. So there's benefit not only from just eating more plants, but also from replacing some less-healthy foods with those plant foods.

Lower Blood Pressure

Most people living a plant-based diet automatically have lower blood pressure due to a higher intake of potassium-rich foods. Potassium helps lower blood pressure that leads to stress and anxiety. Most all whole grains, legumes, nuts, seeds, and all fruits and vegetables contain high amounts of potassium and Vitamin B6 (which also helps lower blood pressure). Meat and most all animal foods contain little to no potassium and actually raise blood pressure and cholesterol.

Lower Cholesterol

Speaking of lower cholesterol, it's one of the main benefits you'll receive from embracing plant-based foods. Most people don't know that plants contain NO cholesterol, even saturated sources like coconut and cacao. While you should balance your fat intake no matter if you're vegan or not, a plant-based diet is one of the simplest ways to lower cholesterol. Consider this: one egg has twice the amount of cholesterol as a fast food hamburger and fish contains almost or even more cholesterol than meat or poultry, depending on the type you eat. Plant foods like vegetables, fruits, whole grains, nuts, and seeds can actually lower rates of cholesterol and heart disease. For more on taking care of your cholesterol, check out these great tips to take care of your cholesterol on a vegan diet. It can reduce breast-cancer risk

Teenage girls and young women who eat more high-fiber foods—particularly fruits and vegetables—may have a significantly reduced risk of breast cancer later in life, according to results from an analysis of more than 90,000 women from the Nurses' Health Study.

It can reduce painful symptoms of arthritis

A veg diet lessens inflammation and arthritis symptoms, according to Nathan Wei, MD, director of the Arthritis Treatment Center in Frederick, MD. Meat-free diets decrease the production of proteins like cytokines that cause

or aggravate inflammation.

And best of all, it can extend your life

A study conducted by researchers at Loma Linda University, in California, followed 73,000 Seventh-day Adventists between 2002 and 2007 and found that a vegetarian diet is associated with lower mortality—from all causes—than all other diets.

Alzheimer's & Neurodegenerative Disease

Believe it or not, even Alzheimer's and neurodegenerative disease patients can benefit from a plant-based diet. While there are few documented cases of reversal, most are preventable. In fact, a comprehensive report conducted by husband and wife team, Drs. Dean and Ayesha Sherzai concluded that over 90% of Alzheimer's cases are preventable.

Much of this prevention is achievable with lifestyle strategies, and whole foods plant-based nutrition is one of the most consequential strategies of all. Additional research has shown that this may be due in part to the brain-gut connection. A poor diet disrupts the gut microbiota, contributing to inflammation in the body and affecting the central nervous system and, ultimately, the brain. One study found that inflammation, gut dysbiosis, and leaky gut may contribute to the process of neurodegeneration in Alzheimer's patients.

Nuts

A major study published in the New England Journal of Medicine showed that people who ate nuts significantly reduced their risk of cancer (and overall mortality) compared to people who ate few or no nuts. Additionally, the American Society of Clinical Oncology released a report of more than 800 patients with stage III colon cancer. They found that eating nuts can make a significant difference in overall cancer survival. In the study, those who consumed about two small handfuls (about 2 ounces) of tree nuts per week had a 46% lower chance of cancer recurrence and a 53% lower chance of death than those who did not eat nuts.

Cooked Tomatoes

The cancer-fighting power of tomatoes may be attributable to lycopene, a cancer-starving antioxidant. Studies show that men who eat two to three cups of cooked tomatoes twice weekly have a 30% lowered risk of prostate cancer.

Purple Potatoes

Once a food of the Incan kings, purple potatoes contain a natural chemical called anthocyanin, which starves and kills cancer cells — and wipes out the dreaded cancer stem cells.

Mushrooms

Researchers from the University of Western Australia in Perth conducted a study of 2,000 Chinese women. (About half had suffered from breast cancer.) The scientists reviewed the women's eating habits and factored out other variables that contribute to cancer, such as being overweight, lack of exercise, and smoking. They came to a startling finding about mushrooms. Women who consumed at least a third of an ounce of fresh mushrooms every day (about one mushroom per day) were 64% less likely to develop breast cancer. When those same women also drank green tea daily, they reduced their risk of breast cancer by 89%.

Obesity

Rates of obesity are at an all-time high around the world. In the U.S. alone, over 39% of the population is suffering from obesity. Eating a plant-based diet helps fight obesity, too.

A 16-week randomized clinical trial showed that a plant-based vegan diet contributes to a reduction in body weight, fat mass, and insulin resistance. And a study published in the British Journal of Nutrition concluded that each additional year of adopting a vegan diet decreased the risk of obesity by 7%. That's nothing to sneeze at.

Plant-Based Diet Benefits to the Environment

Adopting a plant-based diet isn't just good for your health; it's also good for our planet. Cycling calories through livestock is much less efficient than eating them directly. It takes about 12 pounds of grain or soy to produce one pound of feedlot beef. For pork, it takes about seven pounds of feed to produce one pound of edible meat, and for chicken, about four. No wonder 80% of the world's soy crop and 70% of the grain grown in the U.S. is being fed to feed livestock.

Animal agriculture is, essentially, a protein factory in reverse.

Worldwide, about eight times as much land is used to grow food for animals as is used to grow food for humans. Huge tracts of forest are being cut down to make way for factory farms, areas for cows to graze, or fields to grow animal feed.

If the world, just hypothetically, went vegan, we'd free up 75% of the globe's agricultural land — an area the size of the

United States, Australia, the European Union, China, and India combined. That land could be used to grow food for a rapidly expanding human population, could be planted with trees or other vegetation to absorb carbon out of the atmosphere, could be returned to wildlife, or could be used for many other purposes.

Current practices in animal agriculture contribute significantly to global greenhouse gas emissions, too. And while CO2 is one major factor, it isn't the only one. As National Geographic puts it, methane, the gas that comes "...out of a cow's plumbing," is even more efficient than CO2 at trapping heat. Twenty-eight times more powerful, to be exact. Not only that but in a world facing a potentially irreversible climate crisis, methane dissipates much more rapidly than CO2. That means changing your diet today will reduce your carbon footprint immediately. According to an Oxford University study, going vegetarian or vegan can cut your carbon footprint in half.

CHAPTER TWO

WHAT YOU WILL BE EATING

What YouWill Be Eating If You Can One Plant Based Diet

When picturing what a plant-based meal looks like, fruits and vegetables probably come to mind. And they're an important part of just about any healthy diet. But you're not limited to these foods. There are a wide variety of plant foods to enjoy.

The major types of food typically eaten on a plant-based diet include:

Fruits — Ex: Apples, berries, kiwis, mangoes, avocado, bananas, jackfruit, etc.

Vegetables — Ex: Onions, broccoli, beets, potatoes, mushrooms, carrots, etc.

Whole grains — Ex: Quinoa, millet, buckwheat, wheat, rice, corn, etc.

Beans & legumes — Ex: Black beans, chickpeas, lentils, edamame, peas, etc.

Nuts & seeds — Ex: Almonds, cashews, chia seeds, flaxseeds, walnuts, etc.

Herbs & spices — Ex: Turmeric, ginger, cinnamon, oregano, garlic, cayenne, etc.

Fermented foods — Ex: Kimchi, sauerkraut, miso, natto, etc.

Eating across all these food groups will help you get an abundance of micronutrients from your food. Also, when choosing from each category, think "eat the rainbow." Colorful plant foods are full of phytochemicals (a fancy word that just means "chemicals from plants) and antioxidants that are good for keeping different parts of your body healthy.

Another easy way to eat the healthiest combination of plant foods is by remembering an acronym coined by Dr. Joel Fuhrman: GBOMBS. GBOMBS stands for: greens, beans, onions, mushrooms, berries, and seeds.

What Do You Avoid on a Plant-Based Diet?

When choosing to eat a plant-based diet, you'll want to focus mainly on fresh foods. In a grocery store, that means primarily shopping the outer aisles. If possible, choose organic foods as much as possible to avoid exposure to GMOs and pesticides.

However, the main foods you should avoid on a plant-based diet are:

Most or all animal products (Especially factory-farmed meat, eggs, & dairy products)

Refined sugars (White sugar, cane sugar, high fructose corn syrup, chemical-based calorie-free sweeteners, etc.)

Highly processed vegetable oils (Corn oil, cottonseed oil, sunflower oil, peanut oil, soybean oil, etc.)

White flour (Especially bleached white flour which is full of chemicals and heavy metals — and virtually devoid of nutrition)

Junk food (Including most cookies, chips, crackers, snack bars, sweetened drinks, packaged foods, etc.)

GMOs (The primary genetically engineered crops are corn, soy, canola, sugar beets, cotton, and alfalfa — plus a bit of apple, zucchini, and potato)

You'll also want to pay special attention to nutrition labels. By reading labels, you can avoid ultra-processed and harmful ingredients. Packaged foods should have as few ingredients as possible. As a general rule, if you can't pronounce an ingredient, or don't know what it is, put the food back.

Many packaged foods are full of health claims like "all-natural" or "non-GMO." But most of these phrases are branding tactics meant to mislead consumers into thinking a product is healthy. This is called "greenwashing."

What About Gluten & Grains?

For most people, grains can be part of a healthy, plant-based diet. Some of my favorites are quinoa, millet, amaranth, buckwheat, oats, and teff. In many studies, whole grains have been shown to help fight heart disease, type 2 diabetes, cancer, and even obesity. But not everything is peachy in grain land.

Most of the grains eaten in the world today are sprayed with pesticides, and some crops, especially wheat, may even be treated with glyphosate as a desiccant (to dry the crop out before harvest). Corn, unless it's grown organically, is often genetically engineered. Then there's rice, which, while popular, is often contaminated with a disturbing amount of arsenic.

For some medical conditions, like autoimmune diseases, grains can also cause inflammation in the gut and contribute to symptoms. This is especially true with the gluten present in wheat. Although only about 1% of the world's population has diagnosed celiac disease, many more show signs of gluten intolerance with symptoms like headaches, joint pain, skin problems, seizures, and digestive issues. If you're facing any of these symptoms, it can be helpful to go gluten-free for three to six months and see if they clear up.

While many people have jumped on the gluten-free bandwagon, that doesn't mean it's necessarily best for everyone. A few studies actually show health benefits from eating whole grain wheat products.

If you're going to eat wheat, though, you might want to look for 100% whole wheat (since white flour doesn't do your body any favors!), and aim to make sure your grains are organically grown, so you can avoid glyphosate contamination.

Can You Get All the Nutrients You Need on a Plant-Based Diet?

As you begin your journey on a plant-based diet, you may start to get questions from friends and family. Any time you eat differently than the norm, you're bound to get some pushback.

It's like, you could eat fast food for every meal for 10 years and nobody will bat an eye. But trade a fried chicken meal for a green salad topped with sunflower seeds, and everybody suddenly worries about you shriveling up and wasting away.

You may hear, "Why are you eating that?" Or, "Why aren't you eating that?" But some of the most frequently asked questions you might encounter on a plant-based diet have to do with nutrients. "Where do you get your protein?" Or "Where do you get your calcium or iron?" And recently, the meat, dairy, and egg industries rolled out a new propaganda playbook at the July 2019 meetings of the Dietary Guidelines Advisory Committee of the U.S. government. Their goal? Scare people into eating lots of animal products for fear of choline deficiency.

Many people believe you can't get all the nutrients you need without animal products. But plants have protein, calcium, and iron in abundance, in addition to a host of other vitamins, minerals, and antioxidants. (And yes, many plants are abundant sources of choline.) In actuality, people these days are far more likely to be deficient in fiber than protein: Only 3% of Americans get their daily amount of recommended fiber. But that's not a problem when you're eating mostly plants!

Still, if you're wondering how much protein, iron, or calcium you really need, and what plant-based foods to get them from, read below

Protein: Plant-Based Protein: What You Need to Know

Calcium: The Healthiest Way to Get the Calcium You Need + 9 Calcium-Rich Foods

Iron: The Truth About Iron + Why Plant-Based Foods Are the Best Way to Get the Iron You Need

Are Supplements Necessary?

No matter how you choose to eat, in the modern world, most diets are lacking in something. In the case of plant-based diets, there are a few nutrients that are especially important to pay attention to.

They are:

1) Vitamin B12
2) Vitamin D3
3) Omega-3 fatty acids
4) Vitamin K2
5) Zinc

In the case of these nutrients, supplements may be necessary to avoid a deficiency.

Fill Your Plate with Plants

Approximately 54% of calories in the standard American diet come from processed foods, while another 34% come from animal products. While research has shown just how detrimental these foods are to your health, federal nutrition guidelines have yet to catch up. It wasn't until 2011 that the USDA replaced their meat food group with a generic "protein" one. And while their My Plate guidelines are certainly an improvement over past recommendations, it's still not exactly the optimal balance of nutrition.

Physicians Committee for Responsible Medicine created the Power Plate, which provides another take on what a healthy plate really looks like. Spoiler alert: It's full of plants! The Power Plate recommends meals consisting of a balance between fruits, vegetables, legumes, and grains.

Communicate When Eating Out

Eating out at restaurants, or when visiting friends and family, presents its own set of challenges.

Unless you're going to a restaurant that specializes in vegan, vegetarian, or plant-based food, you may struggle with finding completely plant-based options. Let whomever you're dining with know your dietary preferences and see if you can find someplace that suits you both. Use apps and websites like Yelp or Happy Cow to find plant-based eateries.

Looking at menus ahead of time can also help. And when at a restaurant, ask questions about food preparation methods and substitutions. Most restaurants will do their best to accommodate your request.

Similarly, when going to parties and dinners with family and friends, let your host know your dietary needs ahead of time. In extreme circumstances, you could also offer to bring your own food or even to eat beforehand.

Take it One Step at a Time

If you decide to try a plant-based lifestyle, take it one step at a time. You may decide to go "cold turkey," but you can also go slower if that feels easier and more sustainable to you. Go at the pace that feels right for you, as you add in new things and steer clear of others. What's most important is that you keep taking steps for your health and the health of the planet — and then take more steps, as you build momentum. This isn't about a diet or a fad. It's about laying the groundwork for a new way of life. At the end of the day, it's your habits that help to shape your destiny.

CHAPTER THREE

TIPS FOR PLANT BASED DIET

12 Tips on How to Start a Plant-Based Diet

Chances are you've come in touch with one or more benefits of a plant-based diet at this point. Recent media coverage, as well as some major documentaries, have shed light on how shifting towards more wholesome vegan meals not only heals our bodies but also the planet as a whole – while saving countless innocent lives.

If any of these arguments for starting a plant-based diet have intrigued you, one of your next thoughts might probably be:

"wow but this seems so overwhelming, how do I even start?"

Make no mistake, we went through all of the yucky plant-based milk and cheese options (they do exist!) to find our favorites... but we were dedicated to making this shift for ourselves and the animals.

And if you find a strong reason to start taking this journey, we're sure that you can endure some trial and error along the way, too.

From finding some new favorite recipes to accidentally eating something with milk powder (they put this stuff everywhere nowadays!) and having to explain to your friends and family how you can actually survive without cheese – all of these wonderful moments can become reality.

The vegan trend is no secret anymore and we believe that now it's easier than ever to make the switch. Especially since so many others have carved a path for you to follow and navigate things with ease.

How to Start a Plant-Based Diet

Although we could have written so much more in this book, we decided to just stick to these following 12 tips on how you can start a plant-based diet! Come on board – we promise it'll be easier and more fun than you might think.

1. What's Your Motivation?

Since you made your way to read this book, you are probably in a stage of your life where you are ready for some major changes.

Now, just take a second and become very clear about the goals you want to achieve by hopping on this plant-based lifestyle. What is important to you?

Maybe you want to get rid of some kind of disease, increase your energy, help save the planet or animal lives – it doesn't matter. Anything that excites you to take further steps towards a plant-based diet is great.

Keep it close to your heart, write it down, research it regularly to stay in touch with your motivation and learn something new along the way... because the reasons for not eating animal products are endless and you might resonate with more and more over time.

You could watch some documentaries or YouTube videos to keep focused even when things get a little harder.

2. Eat a Lot of Food

This is something that confuses many in the beginning and can be different to everyone. Depending on what you were used to eating, the size of your meals will increase a lot!

Especially if you come from a diet high in animal products and processed foods, you really have to up your quantities when switching over to a plant-based diet.

That's because fruits, veggies, grains and legumes are less calorically dense compared to butter, cheese, eggs and meat. This is true especially when you focus on whole foods and lower fat plant-based foods.

So, load up on baked potatoes, quinoa, beans, salad and fresh fruit! If you struggle to eat larger portions, replace some of the veggies (especially raw veggies) with things like nut butter, seeds, avocado, pasta, bread or tofu to ensure you get enough calories and nutrients.

If you tend to have an insatiable hunger, then a whole food plant-based diet really is for you! Due to the high fiber and water content, it'll be hard to gain a lot of weight. Especially for those who come from a restrictive eating background, it's important to remember to eat to your heart's content and never deprive yourself.

This isn't about 'everything in moderation', it's about living abundantly off the good stuff. Over time, your body will get used to these kinds of volumes.

Remember that everyone needs a different amount of calories each day and although we'd love for you to free yourself from tracking your intake, it can be a good idea to do so in the beginning to get a feel for plant-based foods – and to see how much you can actually eat!

Try to get rid of the 1200-1600 calories per day mindset and rely more on your natural hunger and satiety cues.

3. Surround Yourself with Healthy Foods

Guess what, you cannot eat what you don't buy or have around you! Simple but true. Create a supportive environment by keeping your home as clean as possible.

This means browsing your kitchen in search of any food that isn't beneficial to you or that you plan on not eating anymore – either give it to someone else who'd like to eat it or simply toss it to not be tempted (we like to use local food sharing groups to donate the food we don't want to consume).

Don't keep it just because you've already bought it and think it'd be a waste not to use it. Your body is not a garbage bin!

The next step in helping yourself change your ways is to buy heaps of fruits and vegetables, potatoes and rice, beans, or nuts, so you're always able to prepare healthy meals and snacks.

Starches like whole grains, potatoes, pumpkin and legumes are your number one source of energy, so make sure you always have plenty of those within reach.

Produce can also be bought frozen instead of fresh to prevent food waste – plus you always have something in the freezer to whip up a quick and well-rounded meal.

All of these foods, although they are healthy and unprocessed, have a pretty long shelf life which makes them very convenient.

4. Prepare for Being on the Go

It's one thing to eat plant-based at home but what if hunger hits and you're out and about? Instead of ravenously looking for something that you could eat and being tempted to just grab a highly processed or animal-based option, you could make sure to always have some kind of snack with you.

This could mean some fresh fruit, nuts, energy balls or vegan bars – but also homemade wraps, sandwiches, grain-based salads or simply leftovers.

Other tips here would be to eat before you leave the house and know of a few locations you can grab some good plant-based meals or snacks.

5. Make Food Swaps

Our advice is generally to take a gentle approach and slowly but steadily add more plant-based foods into your diet. We don't restrict, we replace!

Swap some of your favorite processed or animal-based food for a healthy alternative. For instance, to veganize your meals you could use avocado instead of butter, tofu instead of chicken and black bean burgers instead of beef.

To make more wholesome plant-based choices, have dates instead of white sugar, use whole grain instead of white flour spaghetti and have fruit as a snack.

Increase the amount of healthy vegan ingredients in your meals until you've crowded out the bad stuff.

Start with a Plant-Based Breakfast

Three vegan main meals per day can seem a bit daunting when you're just starting out. But how does a fruity loaded oatmeal for breakfast sound? It's just one delicious, easy and healthy way to start your day.

Usually, breakfasts are the easiest meals to veganize. Think pancakes, chia pudding, peanut butter and jelly sandwich or savory options such as tofu scrambles with potatoes or avocado toast.

And there are a lot more vegan breakfast options out there such as our easy recipes for:

1) Fluffy blueberry muffins
2) Raspberry banana bread
3) Easy gluten-free oat bars
4) Strawberry protein smoothie

These easy plant-based breakfasts will inspire you to move on to a healthy vegan lunch, which is the next meal you can tackle. Once you feel confident to have a fully plant-based breakfast and lunch, move on to dinner.

6. Educate Yourself

There is a lot of misinformation out there and you will run into more than just one conversation about how unhealthy, complicated or useless a vegan diet is.

We've all been taught that animal products are part of a proper diet and it's understandable that people around you are opposed to the idea of eating only plants. Whether it's real concern, curiosity or being offended on their part, having a few facts on hand is always a good idea

Lots of huge organizations like the American Dietetic Association have stated that properly planned vegan diets are healthy for all stages of life, lots of doctors and dietitians recommend eating a plant-based diet for the prevention of chronic diseases – plus there are anecdotes and real-life examples of people thriving on plants.

7. Find Like-Minded People

Human beings are social creatures. We're highly impacted by the people we surround ourselves with and one of the most common reasons for why vegans go back to animal products again is social pressure.

Feeling alone in your quest and having to justify, organize and explain yourself over and over again can become so tiring, and, in the end – not worth it anymore.

As much as we want to inspire not-yet-vegans to try plant-based eating for a while and take a look at the reasons behind veganism, we also want to prevent more ex-vegans.

We often hear from our readers that they don't have any support at home from their families – which is why we highly recommend reaching out online and joining a virtual vegan group somewhere.

A good place to start would be Facebook (you're always welcome in our private group here) where you can search for vegan or plant-based groups – some of which might even be in your local area!

Having someone to talk to about delicious plant-based food and have the opportunity to rant, or ask for help if you're looking for a specific product, is invaluable. There are many other platforms like Meetup to get in touch with like-minded people in real life.

After a while, you might even influence some friends or family members to try more plant-based meals and get an ally that way – who knows. Let the results speak for themselves and people will become curious at some point. We definitely are a growing movement, so let's all connect!

8. Equip Your Kitchen

Similar to stocking up on plant-based staple foods, you should also make sure to have some basic kitchen tools at home.

From things like a cutting board, sharp knives, baking sheets, pots and a nonstick pan to a small immersion blender or personal blender, pressure cooker and spiralizer – these tools will open up a huge world of meals you can create.

No need to spend a ton of money, you can ask around if someone has a spare tool or can lend you a specific one to see if you'd become a regular user.

Sometimes, you can also get a good deal over at Amazon or other online stores if you keep an eye on an item you'd love to get.

10 Gently Create New Habits

Be loving and kind to yourself. If you haven't reached your goals yet or feel like you're not doing things perfectly, don't beat yourself up. Keep your dreams and visions in mind and work towards them, but accept where you are right now and take it step by step.

Your thoughts have a bigger impact on your perception and reality as you might think. It all just comes down to creating new habits so eating a plant-based diet feels like second nature to you.

Putting yourself down or under pressure can cause a spiral of negative beliefs and events, so don't forget about the big scheme of things and adjust your expectations according to your own pace. When you become your biggest fan and supporter, your success is much more likely.

Go back to some of the tips above and take things meal by meal.

11. Keep Things Fun & Exciting

Once you have dabbled in vegan waters and tried to make plant-based versions of your favorite meals, you can take it one step further. There are probably quite a few dishes you've never even heard of or foods you haven't tried.

During your next visit to the supermarket, pay attention to all the different types of fruits, veggies, beans, lentils, grains, nuts and seeds and choose one or a few that look interesting and which you have never eaten before.

12. Make a Solid Commitment

Now that you have created a good foundation for your plant-based lifestyle, it's time to commit. Choose a few weeks or a month during which you'll try to put everything into action and really follow through.

Clean out your kitchen or kitchen space, have all kinds of plant-based staples on hand, keep a list with your favorite plant-based meals and snacks around, and enjoy every single bite!

Maybe following some fellow vegans on social media could give you some additional inspiration and help you feel less alone.

It's only when you decide to make this happen that the transformation will take place and you'll be able to recognize all of the amazing benefits of living this way.

Bonus: Free Vegan Transition

Jumping into a 100% whole food plant-based diet overnight may work for some, but it takes a lot of improvising and willpower to stay on track. The change can be so overwhelming that many fall off the wagon after a couple of days and head back to animal products and junk food.

Of course, this is highly dependent on where you're coming from! For example, the transition won't be so bad if you are already on a diet that is rich in fruits, veggies, grains, and legumes.

Both our own experiences and stories from countless other people in the movement have proven time and time again that a gentle approach to changing one's diet is much more sustainable. Because we want you to succeed and reach your personal goals, we put together a free 6-part course where we give you even more guidance and hands-on advic

How to Eat a Lot and Still Lose Weight

2 out of 3 Americans are overweight or obese and other, even less developed, countries seem to follow this trend.

Even though doctors and the media have been trying to help us shed some excess pounds, it's somehow not working. Their mantra is that we should "eat less and move more." If this led to sustainable weight loss, we would never struggle while being on restrictive diets and be already thin by now. But we need enough food to get through the day. So how can we eat a lot and still lose weight?

Unfortunately, many diet plans focus on restrictions and use guidelines such as "just cut calories", "don't eat carbs" or "reduce your portions".

However, it has been shown that adding foods that are low in calorie density is the best strategy for losing weight – not just eating less overall.

Long term studies on low calorie dense diets have shown that those who made the greatest reductions in the calorie density of their diets lost the most weight. They also consumed the most volume and weight of food, which helped them to control hunger and kept them satisfied.

Overall, these participants ate the healthiest diets which naturally consisted of high amounts of fiber, vitamins, and minerals, and only small amounts of saturated fat.

So they ate more food, were more satisfied, lost more excess weight, and lowered their disease-risk without restricting or counting calories. It almost sounds too good to be true!

Eater smarter, not less, is the solution to weight management!

The secret to these results starts with the principles of calorie density. So let's take a closer look and see how to eat a lot and still lose weight.

What Is Calorie Density?

Calorie density is simply a measure of the concentration of calories in a particular food. The higher the calorie density, the higher the concentration of calories packed into the food bite for bite.

This can be helpful to roughly estimate the amount of calories that are on your plate but also to learn which foods to emphasize to reach your weight goals.

Coincidentally, foods that are low in calories are also generally rich in essential nutrients and lead us to good health. This doesn't mean that all calorie dense foods are very unhealthy, as you will see later, but they tend to cause you to overeat as they pack a lot of calories into each bite.

It's our natural tendency to reach for the calorie dense foods (an evolutionary survival mechanism) and our brains also reward us more for snacking on chocolate compared to an apple. It's less chewing and digesting for more energy!

General Compositions

Foods that are low in calorie density, like fruits, vegetables, whole grains and legumes, don't pack a lot of calories per bite. Their molecular composition allows you to fill up on them while unintentionally eating fewer calories – therefore, losing weight without going hungry. This is because they are

1) High in fiber
2) High in water
3) Low in fat

On the other hand, foods that are high in calorie density, like processed food or animal-based food, are stuffed with lots of calories per bite while offering very little bulk or volume – which can easily lead to an overconsumption of calories. This is because these foods are generally

1) Low in fiber
2) Low in water
3) High in fat
4) High in added sugar

As you can see, there are some key factors that make a food high or low in calorie density and therefore generally better or worse for weight loss and healthy weight maintenance.

The 4 Categories of Calorie Density

If all of this sounds a bit confusing and unclear to you at this point, no worries. We created four different categories that help you remember the approximate calorie density of a specific food.

It's a hands-on approach to this fantastic scientific concept and you can use the categories to easily create weight loss-friendly meals.

1. Low Calorie Density

All fruits and vegetables, such as apples, bananas, berries, kale, zucchini, and bell peppers. Exceptions: dried fruit and fruit juice where the fiber and water content have been manipulated. You can eat freely from these foods if you want to lose weight.

2. Moderate Calorie Density

All starchy vegetables like potatoes, peas and corn as well as intact whole grains like brown rice and oats, and legumes like beans and lentils. You can eat a relatively large portion of these foods, we recommend they take up around 30-50% of your plate for weight loss.

3. High Calorie Density

Slightly processed plant-based foods like bagels, dry cereal, bread, tortillas, and dried fruit. (Meat and cheese would be in this category as well but please read below why we don't recommend any animal products.) Limit the consumption of these foods.

4. Very High Calorie Density

Nuts and seeds, oils and fats, chocolate, and junk foods. Greatly limit or avoid the consumption of these foods. Please note: This doesn't mean that nuts and seeds are unhealthy, they are just high in calories.

The first 2 groups (low and moderate in calorie density) should make up the majority of your calorie intake. But the ratio of vegetables or fruits to starches can also be an important factor.

We all know that eating a large bowl of lettuce might fill up your stomach, but it will keep you hungry at the same time. So make sure to combine your low calorie dense foods with some starches from the second category to feel satiated and have enough energy to go about your day.

5. Real-Life Eating Tips for Weight LosS

Now, we want to break all of this down into some actionable steps for you. Although the overall message is to just eat more of the low calorie density food and cut out or reduce the ones that are very high in calorie density, different small shifts can help you get there.

1. Hunger & Satiety

Whenever you are hungry, eat until you are comfortably full and choose food lower in calorie density. Don't starve or stuff yourself, and don't eat when you're not hungry. Likewise, don't let yourself get too hungry because you're more likely to overeat or eat junk food in these situations.

2. Sequence Meals

Start all meals with a salad, soup or fruit. These foods will already partially fill your stomach and lower the overall calorie density of your meal, whatever you choose to eat afterward.

3. Don't Drink Your Calories

Liquid calories like soft drinks or even fruit juice offer little if any satiety, so they don't fill you up as much as solid foods with the same amount of calories. Even fruit smoothies could hinder your weight loss if they consist of more fruit than you could eat hadn't it been blended up.

4. Create a Smart Ratio

Dilute the calorie density of your meals by filling at least half your plate (by visual volume) with some food lowest in calorie density, which are non-starchy vegetables and fruits.

5. Keep the Categories in Mind

Non-starchy vegetables have the lowest and oils have the highest calorie density. Therefore, adding non-starchy vegetables to any dish will always lower the overall calorie density of a meal. Consequently, adding fat or oil to any dish will always raise the overall calorie density of a meal.

6. Limit High Calorie Dense Food

If you use flour products or nuts and seeds, integrate them into meals that are made of low calorie dense foods and think of them as condiments. For example, add a few walnuts or raisins to a bowl of oatmeal with fruit.

Full Guide to Sustainable Weight Loss

Calorie density is just one part of getting a lean body for good. Putting all of what we know about easy and healthy weight loss on a plant-based diet into one article just wouldn't be possible! This is why we decided to write a full guide that will explain what kind of strategy is absolutely perfect for effortless weight loss.

You'll basically get all the tools you need to not only lose weight but also improve your health and feel satisfied, satiated and energized at the same time.

From educational passages, motivating studies and easy-to-follow steps to short summaries, worksheets, dozens of satisfying weight loss recipes, and a fully laid-out 21-day meal plan: Everything will work in perfect synergy to set you up for success.

Your Ultimate Guide to Plant-Based Kitchen Tools

When focusing most of your meals around fruits, vegetables, grains and legumes, you need different equipment than, let's say, a tenderizer (although a sharp knife will be useful in any case).

Whether you're just starting out on a plant-based diet or are looking for ways to reignite your spark in the kitchen, the kitchen tools list will guide towards your next favorite gadgets.

Because having the right cooking equipment can make or break your mealtimes, and this is especially true when following a healthy plant-based diet. We do have less convenience food to fall back on and that's not necessarily a bad thing.

With the right tools to hand you can make every meal a restaurant-worthy delight, with lots of color, flavor and variety throughout the week.

For most people cooking can feel like a chore, which is why the typical Western diets often consist of microwave meals, takeout and processed snacks. If you want to add more fresh, whole plant foods into your diet, you'll need to spend a little more time in the kitchen.

But don't worry! Cooking doesn't have to be the exhausting time-sap most people think it is.

With an open mind, a positive attitude and the right kitchen equipment, you'd be

Better yet, if you have kids you can easily get them involved with both the shopping and preparing of their meals, making it a learning experience during which they get to discover new and exciting foods.

The Best Tools for a Plant-Based Kitchen

You're probably wondering how much a well-equipped kitchen would cost, and whether it's even a possibility for you.

The good news is that there's no need to spend lots of money – some of these essentials will likely be already in your kitchen! Then, many tools double up and serve more than one purpose, meaning you can get a lot of value from multi-taskers before thinking about adding another tool to your arsenal.

Some of the more expensive tools in the list can be purchased second-hand or even borrowed from a friend if you need it for a special occasion or would like to try it before buying.

Depending on your preferences, you will find yourself wanting or needing some of these kitchen tools more than others. For example, you might not require a food processor but would love a mandolin to make your chopping and slicing easier.

Or you may never have use for a coffee grinder, but an air fryer would be your dream. Whatever you choose, think about the tools that would make the most sense for your lifestyle right now and the types of meals you'd like to cook up.

Remember that many food prep and cooking methods such as pressing or steaming can be achieved even if you don't have the specific tool required (as you'll see below). While it may take you a little more time, it is best to simply use what you have; then, as your skills in the kitchen grow, you can splash out on more streamlined items you know you'll use.

Whatever your situation, budget or kitchen size, we believe that healthy, varied, colorful meals can be enjoyed by everyone. Check out the following kitchen tools list for helpful, fun and mostly affordable items that make plant-based eating so much easier – no matter where you're at right now.

Basic Kitchen Tools List

You've probably already started accumulating some helpful basics to prepare your own healthy food in the kitchen. Even these tools alone are enough to create beautiful, satisfying dishes.

Sharp Cutting Knife

Investing in a good chef's knife (or set of knives) is always a great start as they'll be your most-used tools in the kitchen.

Prices vary, so it's possible to find a sharp cutting knife (and serrated knife) to fit your budget. A good knife makes prepping ingredients quick, easy and much safer.

Cutting Board

Cutting boards are handy for chopping and slicing all of your ingredients before you cook them. They can be made from either wood or plastic. It's sometimes a good idea to have a separate cutting board for fragrant veggies like onions and garlic, so they don't affect the flavor of other fruits and veggies.

Small and Large Pot

Having at least one small and one large pot is great for cooking sauces, grains, soups, stews, curries and other dishes. Large pots are great for batch cooking or cooking for the whole family. Having more than one pot makes a lot of sense because you may need to cook a sauce and an accompanying grain or some veggies at the same time.

Non-Stick Pans

A non-stick pan or skillet is a must-have when cooking pancakes or vegan omelets without oil, dry-frying tofu or water-sautéing vegetables as very few non-stick pans last more than a few years we'd suggest not breaking the bank on this. This makes them a very affordable yet effective kitchen addition. We use ours almost daily.

Metal Mixing Bowl

A metal mixing bowl is great for whipping up yummy baked treats, or for tossing salads or whisking pancake batter. Metal bowls are lighter than glass and don't take up a lot of space. We recommend getting some with lids so they double up as food containers!

Kettle

Not just for preparing your favorite tea or filter coffee – a kettle is a real time-saver for boiling veggies or pasta as you can boil water in the kettle first before adding the food to the pot. Some sauces or gravies also require adding boiling water. Plus, who doesn't love a nice hot-water bottle during fall and winter?

Strainer

A fine mesh strainer is essential for draining water from grains, beans and potatoes. But it also has a number of other uses too: getting the pulp out of juice; sifting flour; straining soups, stocks and sauces, and even for steaming vegetables if you don't have a steamer basket.

Whisk

Always handy, whisks are invaluable when it comes to making pancake batter, whipping up a dressing, or getting light, fluffy cake mix. Go for a stainless steel balloon design as it won't transfer off flavors in acidic recipes.

Peeler

Available in differing shapes and designs, a peeler is essential for preparing potatoes, sweet potatoes, carrots and other root vegetables.

Measuring Cups and Spoons

Stop the guessing game and get some measuring cups and spoons. They are very important if you want to follow baking recipes and get the best results every time! Measuring cups are also handy for measuring out oatmeal or grains to know how much water to add when cooking them.

Kitchen Scale

For recipes that don't use cup measurements, a kitchen scale will come in very handy to help you achieve greater precision. You can choose either a digital or analogue design and can use it to translate metric and imperial measurements for any recipe. This is sometimes quicker to do than using measuring cups!

Wooden Spoons

These super traditional utensils are great for stirring sauces and gravies as they cook, or for mixing up cake batter or making oatmeal. The handle won't get hot whilst cooking (making them safe to use) and they also won't mark your non-stick pots and pans.

Tofu Press

While it's possible to press tofu between towels, it can get pretty messy. I've found that a tofu press is really the way to go – it does all the work for you. A tofu press removes water more efficiently and won't dirty your dish towels or require a ton of paper towels. Simply place the tofu in the press over a large container and let the water accumulate.

Immersion Blender

Don't have a high-speed blender? No worries. A common and cheaper tool is an immersion blender which can be used to achieve similar things – to smooth out chunky soups, sauces and stews while they still sit in the pot. You could even use it to make your own whipped coconut cream or vegan mayonnaise! We also use them for fruit smoothies sometimes, to make our own hummus and much more.

Steamer Basket

Steaming your vegetables instead of cooking them in water is a great way to maintain the nutrients. It takes just a little water in the bottom of the pan and the veggies will soften quickly. Every plant-based cook should have one of these!

Stainless Steel Pasta Pot

Cooking your pasta in this pot is effortless. The strainer insert and glass lid add to the ease of cooking and will get dinner on the table in a flash.

Next-Level Kitchen Tools

Once you're acquainted with using the basics, here are some helpful kitchen appliances for creating delicious recipes with a little more adventure!

Salad Spinner

Salads are a staple when you're eating a whole food plant-based diet so being able to wash and spin dry your lettuce is a nice time-saver. You can even prepare your greens ahead of time and they'll stay fresh in the fridge for when you're ready to use them.\

Storage Containers

A set of storage containers is great for leftovers and these clear ones allow you to see what's inside. The heavy-duty click tops keep things from spilling. And with glass, you don't have to worry about any chemicals leaching into your food from plastic.

Mixing Bowls

Everyone needs a good set of mixing bowls for combining ingredients. I particularly like this brand because they each have a lid and a non-stick bottom to help keep them from slipping on the counter.

High-Speed Blender

High-speed blenders are a godsend for creating fresh, healthy smoothies or soups that still have all of the fiber packed in. Some brands can even be used for blending gravies, sauces and dressings for a smoother consistency.

Food Processor

While blenders purify things into a smooth liquid form, food processors are better for breaking things down and combining. So if you're looking to make homemade veggie burgers, energy balls or brownies with beans or chickpeas in them, a food processor will help you get the fine consistency you need while blending the flavors together.

Tongs

Some sturdy tongs can really help when serving up tricky things like noodles or spaghetti, or for picking up hot items like burgers, vegan sausages, falafels, steamed veggies or dumplings.

Slow Cooker (Crock Pot)

Another fantastic time saver, the slow cooker (or crock pot, as it's sometimes called) is a great helper for busy weeks or dinner parties. Using a very low amount of energy, a slow cooker will cook your food over a long period of time (around 4-8 hours) ensuring it reaches the perfect temperature and consistency right when you need it.

Use a slow cooker for making stews, curries, pasta sauces, risottos or even oatmeal in large batches. Simply throw in your ingredients, liquids and spices, put on the lid and select the desired setting. Whether you leave it on overnight or while you're at work, the slow cooker does all the work for you so you can come home to a delicious meal with very little effort.

It's also great when having people over for dinner as food can be cooked in large batches and you're not tied to the kitchen.

Rolling Pin

A rolling pin is essential for making fresh pastry or biscuits at home. While there are other ways to roll out pastry if you don't have one (using a glass, for instance), a wooden rolling pin will give smoother, effortless results and is wide enough to cover the whole pastry at once. Because they're inexpensive, it's definitely worth getting one if you spend a lot of time baking.

French Press

Again, if you're a coffee connoisseur like us then you could be upping your game with a French press (sometimes known as a cafetiere) instead of using instant coffee.

Possibly one of the most popular ways to make coffee, it allows the coffee beans to "bloom" in the boiled water before the plunger is used to delicately strain the flavor and pour into your favorite cup. Plus, you will lower the amount of waste you produce by skipping the paper filter!

Lemon Squeezer

Definitely not an essential by any means, but a lemon squeezer can save you from getting sticky lemon juice all over your hands as well as extracting more juice than you could normally. Anyone else tired of picking out the lemon seeds after squeezing some fresh juice over your food?

Juicer

While some nutritionists disagree about whether vegetable juices are healthy, we think they're a great way to add in some extra vitamins and greens to your diet (so long as they're balanced with fibrous whole food meals).

Buying green juices on the go can get pricey, so making them yourself at home is a real money saver. We'd recommend getting a slow masticating juicer over a centrifugal one as it extracts more of the nutrients and keeps the juice fresher for a longer period of time in the fridge.

Spiralizer

We'd never give up our pasta for zoodles, but spiralizing is actually a fantastic way to sneak more veggies into your diet and into your little ones!

Though spiralizers now come in different shapes and sizes, they all pretty much do the same thing, which is turn sweet potatoes, zucchini, carrots and other veggies into long, beautiful noodles or spaghetti. Throw them into salads, Thai dishes or pasta sauces for a nice alternative.

Cooler

A cooler is a nice addition to your kitchen if you spend a lot of hours in school or at work and need to bring your food with you. Even when you go traveling, having a portable cooler with you in the car can keep you from having to buy crappy snacks at the gas station. This nice to have gadget makes sure that your healthy food is still good after a couple of hours – and can be used as back-up refrigeration if you're entertaining guests and happen to run out of fridge space!

It's Up to You!

I hope you enjoyed and find the plant-based kitchen tools lists u and some other tips useful and found something that sparked your interest in getting back into cooking and prepping more often.

Even by stocking your kitchen with the basics, it can be possible to regularly enjoy fresh, varied and nutritious plant-based meals. However, as your taste buds grow more adventurous and you get more confident in the kitchen, adding a few more purpose-built kitchen utensils can help you save time, effort and clean-up as well as levelling up the taste, quality or nutrition of your food.

CHAPTER FOUR

YOUR NEW BASIC SHOPPING LIST

Your New Basic Shopping List

Plant-Based Shopping is actually easier than you think! This list is intended as a resource to help you get started. Keep in mind that food product formulations do change, so it is wise to read labels.

Fresh Produce (Fruits and Vegetables)

Enjoy a wide variety of fruits and vegetables! Choose plenty of dark leafy greens. Avoid avocados if you have heart disease and use sparingly if you are trying to lose weight.

Beans and Legumes

Enjoy ALL varieties of dried beans and lentils. If you buy canned beans, look for low-sodium or no-salt. If you can't get no-salt added, rinse the beans well with water prior to use.

Nuts, Seeds, and Dried Fruits

Avoid nuts if you have heart disease. Use very sparingly if you are trying to lose weight. If you do choose to purchase nuts, any variety is ok but look for raw and no oil-added. Avoid eating by the handful as they are high fat and high calorie and very easy to overeat. Use nut butters sparingly.

Omega-3 rich chia and flax seeds can used to top cereal and replace eggs in baked goods (1 teaspoon chia or ground flaxseed plus 3 teaspoon water = 1 "egg"). Whole flax seeds are not digested so it is best to buy ground flax seeds or even better, grind them right before use in a coffee grinder. Use other seeds (sesame, pumpkin, sunflower) sparingly.

Most dried fruits are acceptable when they are eaten sparingly and do not have added sugar. Keep in mind they are higher in calories than fresh fruits. If you are diabetic or trying to lose weight, eat fresh fruits rather than dried fruits. Avoid dried banana chips as most are actually fried.

Frozen Foods

All varieties of frozen vegetables and fruits without added oil or dairy ingredients.

Breads

Choose breads that are 100% whole grain with no oil added or less than 10% calories from fat. Enriched wheat flour, unbleached wheat flour, wheat flour, and organic wheat flour are not whole grain. Some options are:

Food for Life Ezekiel 4:9 breads, English muffins, and tortillas

Rudi's Organic Bakery 100% Whole Wheat (not 100% oil-free but very low-fat)

Wegmans Organic Sandwich Breads (all varieties but White Made with Oatmeal which is only half whole grain, these breads are not 100% oil-free but lower fat)

Trader Joe's Whole Wheat Tuscan Pane (double check it is the whole wheat variety)

Wegmans Whole Wheat Flat Bread Pizza Crust (not 100% oil-free but very low-fat)

Trader Joe's Corn and Wheat Tortillas

Dave's Killer Bread

Engine 2 Tortillas (Whole Foods)

Whole Grains

There are a very large variety of whole grains to choose from including: rice, quinoa, farro, spelt, bulgur, millet, hull-less barley, whole grain polenta or coarse cornmeal, oatmeal, teff and more. Whole grain rice options include: short, medium, and long grain, basmati, jasmine, black, wild red and even purple! Choose from any variety but make sure to avoid white rice.

Whole Grain Flours

There are a variety of flours to choose from including:

- Whole wheat pastry flour
- Whole wheat flour
- White whole wheat flour

Other whole grain flours including but not limited to: oat, spelt, barley, amaranth, kamut, rye

You can also use gluten-free flours if wheat allergies are an issue but make sure to read the label carefully that they contain only whole grains. Many gluten-free products are highly processed.

Pastas

Any 100% whole wheat or brown rice pasta (other grains are ok – spelt, quinoa, etc – but read carefully to make sure it is entirely whole grain)

Breakfast Cereals

Choose minimally sweetened, whole grain cold and hot cereals without added oil. Some examples are:

- Steel Cut Oatmeal
- Rolled (Old Fashioned) Oats
- Original Cheerios
- Shredded Wheat (not frosted or otherwise sweetened, Wheat'n Bran variety is fine)
- Grape Nuts
- Wheat Chex
- Bran Flakes
- Store brand of any of the above
- Engine 2 Cereals and Granola
- Non-Dairy "Milks"

Choose unsweetened or minimally sweetened non-dairy beverages. Avoid products with oils in the ingredient list.

Avoid oat non-dairy beverages (very high sugar). Some options are:

- Almond Breeze Original Unsweetened or Vanilla Unsweetened
- Wegmans Almond Beverage, Original Unsweetened and Vanilla Unsweetened
- Wegmans Organic Original Soymilk, Unsweetened
- Trader Joe's Almond Beverage, Original Unsweetened and Vanilla Unsweetened
- Trader Joe's Organic Soy Beverage Unsweetened
- Silk Unsweetened Cashew milk
- Silk Soymilk (except for high sugar varieties: Chocolate, Light Chocolate, and Very Vanilla)
- Silk Unsweetened Original or Unsweetened Vanilla Almond milk
- Engine 2 Almond milk
-

Tomato and Pasta Sauces

Choose sauces with no animal products, no added oil or 10% or fewer calories from fat, minimal sugar, and lower sodium when comparing products.

Prepared Salad Dressings

Choose dressings with no added oil or less than 10% calories from fat, minimal sugar, and lower sodium when comparing products.

Flavor "Boosters"

There are many options to boost the flavor of your food without adding any fat or sugar including:

- Vinegars: Balsamic, white balsamic, flavored balsamic, apple cider vinegar, white wine vinegar, unseasoned rice vinegar, and more
- Citrus juice and zest
- Spices and herbs: Individual spices and sodium free flavor blends (Mrs. Dash), garlic and ginger (fresh or minced in jars without added sodium), fresh herbs
- Mustards: Avoid high sugar honey mustard varieties
- Hot sauces: Use sparingly as many are high sodium (Sriracha, Cholula, Frank's RedHot)
- Capers: Rinse before using to reduce sodium content
- Olives: Choose olives that are not packed in oil, use sparingly as most are high in sodium

Convenience Foods

The following are some options for convenience foods:

- Road's End Organics Dairy Free Mac and Cheese (gluten-free)
- Engine 2 Hummus and Bean Dips
- Engine 2 Frozen Plant Strong Grain Medleys
- McDougall Soups
- Pacific Spicy Kale and Black Bean Soup (shelf stable box)
- Progresso Vegetable Classics Lentil with Roasted Vegetables Soup (trace added oil)
- Trader Joe's Organic Lentil Soup (shelf stable box)

- Healthy Sisters Soup and Bean Works; Black Bean, Tuscan, and other varieties made without the oil, dairy, or meat in some of the suggested prep instructions
- Eden Organic Rice & Beans
- Grainful Meal Kits (all but cheddar flavor)
-
-

Chips and Crackers

There are a variety of options to choose from. Avoid kale and vegetable "chips" made with oil. Also avoid kale chip that are high in fat due to nuts and tahini if you are trying to lose weight.

- Wasa Crispbread
- Ryvita Crispbread
- Edward & Sons Brown Rice Snaps (gluten-free, choose oil-free varieties)
- Le Pain des Fleurs Crispbreads (gluten-free)
- Lundberg Brown Rice Rice Cakes (gluten-free)
- Mary's Gone Crackers Crackers and Pretzels (avoid THINS and cookies; gluten-free, but higher fat due to seeds)
- Engine 2 Crackers & Crisps
- Real Food Corn Thins (gluten-free, choose oil-free varieties)
- Tortilla Chips – no commercially available oil-free option (bake your own chips from oil-free corn tortillas cut in triangles at 350 degrees F for 5-7 minutes per side, try a squeeze of lime juice and a sprinkle of chili powder before baking for more flavor (also works for pita chips, but may need to adjust

baking time) – healthier and you won't over eat them if you have to make them yourself!)

Cheese Substitutes

Try nutritional yeast for sprinkling on pasta and using in recipes for "cheesy" flavor.

For special occasions options include:

Miyoko's Creamery cheeses (choose the no added oil varieties)

Treeline Tree Nut Cheeses

These are high in fat so using sparingly.

Meat Substitutes

- Use as you transition if you want a meaty texture and flavor but avoid using daily:
- Lightlife Gimme Lean and Smart Ground Meatless products (check they are oil-free)
- Westsoy Seitan Wheat Protein Strips, Cubed, or Ground
- Bob's Red Mill Organic Textured Soy Protein
- Sunshine Burgers- all oil free
- Engine 2 Burgers (Whole Foods)

CHAPTER FIVE

YOUR NEW PLANT BASED DIET MENU

Your New Menu

A 7-Day Sample Menu for a Standard Plant-Based Diet

Day 1

Breakfast Tofu scramble

Lunch Cauliflower rice bowl with black beans, corn, avocado, and salsa

Dinner Veggie-topped pizza

Snack Zucchini chips

Day 2

Breakfast Oatmeal-based breakfast muffins

Lunch Tomato basil soup with oyster crackers

Dinner Veggie stir-fry with tofu

Snack Hummus wrap

Day 3

Breakfast Homemade oatmeal bars

Lunch Greek salad with a slice of whole-grain pita bread

Dinner Kale and tofu curry

Snack Cashew yogurt with berries and a scoop of peanut butter

Day 4

Breakfast Breakfast burrito with eggs, peppers, and salsa

Lunch Veggie burger and a side salad

Dinner Cauliflower "steak" with roasted sweet potato fries

Snack Veggies with hummus

Day 5

Breakfast Dairy-free yogurt with berries and granola

Lunch Tomato sandwich with pesto and a drizzle of olive oil

Dinner Whole-wheat pasta with roasted tomatoes

Snack Roasted chickpeas

Day 6

Breakfast Chia seed pudding with fresh berries and a spoonful of almond butter

Lunch Avocado toast

Dinner Vegan mushroom enchiladas

Snack Handful of almonds

Day 7

Breakfast Oatmeal with almond milk

Lunch Quinoa bowl with roasted carrots and sweet potatoes

Dinner Vegetarian chili topped with slices of avocado

Snack Whole-wheat toast topped with peanut butter (1)'

A Final Word on What It Means to Eat a Plant-Based Diet Menu

The plant-based diet is a category of diets that have this in common: "All plant-based diets limit animal-derived foods in favor of plants," Yule says. Instead of a diet centered on meat and dairy, the starring roles are played by vegetables, fruit, and whole grains. It's a fresh, flavorful approach to eating and has been shown to have significant health benefits, including weight loss and disease prevention.

CHAPTER SIX

21 day meal plan

DAY 1

Breakfast: Apple Cinnamon Oatmeal (make enough for Wednesday)

Lunch: Couscous Confetti Salad (make enough for a side with tomorrow's dinner) and Carrot and Red Pepper Soup (make enough for tomorrow's lunch)

Snack: Toast with apple butter and banana (easy option: apple or banana)

Dinner: Hoppin' John Salad and Kwick Kale

DAY 2

Breakfast: Cereal, plant milk (your choice), and banana and berries

Lunch: Vegan veggie burger (use whole grain bread topped with lettuce, tomato, onion, and your

favorite mustard) and cup of Carrot and Red Pepper Soup (leftover from yesterday's lunch)

Snack: Air-popped popcorn topped with curry powder or nutritional yeast

Dinner: Southern Beans and Greens (toss in your leftover black-eyed peas here) with side of Couscous Confetti Salad (leftover from yesterday's lunch)

DAY 3

Breakfast: Apple Cinnamon Oatmeal (leftover from Monday; add sliced banana and consider using agave nectar, a delicious, low-glycemic index sweetener)

Lunch: Hummus and veggie sandwich (use pita or whole grain bread, spread with hummus, and top with lettuce, tomato, cucumbers, and any other veggies you wish)

Snack: Soy yogurt with berries

Dinner: Curried Lentil Soup with leftover Couscous Confetti Salad or a side salad (if you are making your own side salad, think greens, such as romaine or red leaf lettuce topped with tomato, cucumber, onion, broccoli, and your favorite low-fat vegan dressing; an easy pick is balsamic vinegar, which is very easy and a little goes a long way)

DAY 4

Breakfast: Cereal with plant milk (your choice) and fresh or frozen berries

Lunch: Vegan cup of soup (McDougall's or Amy's) with whole grain bread

Snack: Carrots and apple

Dinner: Kickstart DIY (see Kickstart DIY tips at end of menus): couscous, lentil, and kale

DAY 5

Breakfast: Smoothie Day: Fantastic Fruit Smoothie

Lunch: Curried Lentil Soup or Southern Beans and Greens

Snack: Edamame or leftover Hummus with carrots

Dinner: Kickstart Dining Out: Mexican

DAY 6

Breakfast: Blueberry Buckwheat Pancakes and Facon Bacon

Lunch: Easy-Bean Dip with Oven-Baked Tortilla Chips and a side salad (if you are making your own side salad, think greens, such as romaine or red leaf lettuce topped with tomato, cucumber, onion, broccoli, and your favorite low-fat vegan dressing; an easy pick is balsamic vinegar, which is very easy and a little goes a long way)

Dinner: Easy Stir-Fry with Always Great Brown Rice (make extra for tomorrow's breakfast rice pudding; use either frozen veggies or your leftover vegetables from the week)

Dessert: Chocolate Raspberry Mousse

DAY 7

Breakfast: Breakfast Rice Pudding (use leftover brown rice from last night's dinner) or frozen waffles (with berries, banana, or both)

Lunch: Spinach Salad with Orange Sesame Dressing (add garbanzo beans)

Snack: Ambrosia

Dinner: Whole wheat pasta with Simple Marinara Sauce (add broccoli, spinach, and any other leftover veggies)

DAY 8

Breakfast: Cinnamon-Raisin Oatmeal

Lunch: Missing Egg Sandwich (use whole-grain bread and top with lettuce and tomato); add a side of Oven-Baked Tortilla Chips and baby carrots

Snack: Frozen mango chunks (buy a bag of frozen mango or eat fresh ones if available)

Dinner: Barbeque-Style Portobellos over quinoa (quinoa is easy to make and cooks up in no time) with steamed or fresh spinach

DAY 9

Breakfast: Cereal, plant milk, and sliced strawberries on top

Lunch: Kickstart Dining Out: Salad bar gone wild! Here's a suggestion for making salad at salad bar: Choose a green, top with a bean, add a grain and tons of veggies, and choose a low-fat vegan dressing or keep it simple with balsamic vinegar (or make your own salad at home with romaine lettuce, garbanzo beans, cucumber, tomato, and balsamic vinegar)

Snack: Oranges and raisins

Dinner: Simple Bean Tacos with Mexican Corn Salad (use leftover salad for tomorrow's lunch)

Dessert: Berry Mousse

DAY 10

Breakfast: Oatmeal with mango and cinnamon (add plant milk)

Lunch: Veggie burger with leftover Mexican Corn Salad

Snack: Carrot and apple

Dinner: Creamy Broccoli Soup with Quinoa Pilaf

DAY 11

Breakfast: Cereal with plant milk and a banana

Lunch: Leftover Missing Egg Sandwich and cup of leftover Creamy Broccoli Soup

Snack: Fresh grapes

Dinner: Farmhouse Salad and leftover Quinoa Pilaf

DAY 12

Breakfast: Mango Delight Smoothie

Lunch: Baked sweet potato with leftover Farmhouse Salad

Snack: Air-popped popcorn with curry or nutritional yeast

Dinner: Kickstart Dining Out: Japanese (try the seaweed salad, edamame, a vegetable sushi roll, such as a cucumber roll or tofu roll, and miso soup)

DAY 13

Breakfast: Fruited Breakfast Quinoa and Kickstart DIY Smoothie (use plant milk, banana, and any fruit you have around; Kickstart DIY tips)

Lunch: Ethiopian Tomato Salad and Asian Guacamole with pita bread

Snack: Edamame

Dinner: Almost Instant Black Bean Chili and Easy Corn Bread Muffins

DAY 14

Breakfast: Zucchini Scramble and Breakfast Homefries

Lunch: Pasta salad (make leftovers for tomorrow's lunch)

Snack: Fruit salad

Dinner: Kickstart DIY: Beans, greens, and grains (consider using barley, lentils, and any leftover kale or bok choy)

DAY 15

Breakfast: Oatmeal with peaches (thaw frozen peaches)

Lunch: Leftover Pasta Salad with a piece of whole grain bread

Snack: Orange slices

Dinner: Spicy Thai Soup (make extra if you want to work it into lunch this week)

DAY 16

Breakfast: Frozen vegan waffles with peaches and maple syrup or cereal with plant milk and fruit

Lunch: Vegan cup of soup (or leftover Spicy Thai Soup) with baked sweet potato (try adding cinnamon on top of your sweet potato)

Snack: Red Pepper Hummus with raw vegetables or pita bread

Dinner: Buckwheat Pasta with Seitan and side of sautéed kale

Dessert: Chocolate Banana Smoothie

DAY 17

Breakfast: Oatmeal with berries or banana

Lunch: Kickstart Dining Out for Lunch: Chinese cuisine (look for the vegetable and tofu dishes with rice and ask for them to be steamed or sauteed with no or light oil)

Snack: Soy yogurt with fruit

Dinner: Lentil Artichoke Stew

DAY 18

Breakfast: Frozen vegan waffles with Berry Applesauce or cereal with plant milk and fruit

Lunch: Leftover Buckwheat Pasta with Seitan or a veggie burger with whole wheat bread or roll, lettuce, tomato, onions, and mustard

Snack: Frozen grapes

Dinner: Zippy Yams and Bok Choy with Always Great Brown Rice

DAY 19

Breakfast: Green Goodie Smoothie

Lunch: Tomato, Cucumber and Basil Salad with add can of garbanzo beans

Snack: Berry Applesauce (leftover from yesterday or just eat an apple) Dinner: Kickstart Dining Out: Italian

DAY 20

Breakfast: Spinach and Mushroom Frittata with side of fruit

Lunch: Quickie Quesadillas

Snack: Air-popped popcorn with curry powder or nutritional yeast

Dinner: Chunky Ratatouille Sauce (save some sauce for lunch tomorrow) served over a grain, like pasta, brown rice, couscous, quinoa, or orzo

DAY 21

Breakfast: Banana Oat French Toast with soysage (try Gimme Lean or another vegan brand)

Lunch: Homemade loaded baked potato with leftover Chunky Ratatouille Sauce or make your own toppings, such as salsa, steamed broccoli, and black beans

Snack: Cantaloupe or another available fruit

Dinner: Hearty Chili Mac with leftover mushrooms and spinach from yesterday's Spinach and Mushroom Frittata

Dessert: Blueberry Muffins (make enough to have for breakfast or a snack this week)

Additional Information for Success

Kickstart DIY:

DIY is short for a do-it-yourself recipe. We want you to get into the habit of going out on your own and making meals without a recipe. If you are not feeling ready for a DIY meal, stick to a recipe. But if you are, grab that can of beans, cook up some brown rice, and top with cooked greens or some frozen mixed vegetables. Or mix your favorite fruits together and toss with soy yogurt. Let your imagination run wild with Kick start DIY meals.

Serving Sizes:

Don't worry too much about the serving sizes of beans, grains, fruits, and vegetables. Thanks to the fiber and low-fat content, you would be hard-pressed to consume more calories than you need from these four food groups. (Exceptions include avocados, olives, etc.)

Cereal:

Look for around 5 grams of fiber per serving. Avoid those that add chemical preservatives, sugar, corn syrup, and/or cane juice.

Bread:

Look for around 4 grams of fiber per slice/serving. Avoid additives such as whey, sugar, corn syrup, caramel colorings, etc.

Jam:

Choose all-fruit jams. These are usually not sweetened with sugar.

Beans:

All beans are great. Buying them dried may be more economical, but you have to plan for the rinsing, soaking, and draining process. Canned and frozen are every bit as good.

Grains:

Whole grains are preferred, but as long as the ones you choose have some fiber you are fine.

Fruits:

All fruits are good: whole fresh, frozen, or dried. Avoid those with added sugar and those that have the fiber removed, e.g., juiced.

Vegetables:

All vegetables are good: whole fresh, frozen, or canned.

CHAPTER SEVEN

BREAKFAST RECIPES
CHICKPEA OMELET

This wonderful egg-free omelet is easy to make and is good for breakfast, lunch, or dinner.

Ingredients

1 cup chickpea flour

½ teaspoon onion powder

½ teaspoon garlic powder

¼ teaspoon white pepper

¼ teaspoon black pepper

1/3 cup nutritional yeast

½ teaspoon baking soda

3 green onions (white and green parts), chopped

4 ounces sautéed mushrooms (optional)

Instructions

1. Combine the chickpea flour, onion powder, garlic powder, white pepper, black pepper, nutritional yeast, and baking soda in a small bowl. Add 1 cup water and stir until the batter is smooth.
2. Heat a frying pan over medium heat. Pour the batter into the pan, as if making pancakes. Sprinkle 1 to 2 tablespoons of the green onions and mushrooms into the batter for each omelet as it cooks. Flip the omelet. When the underside is browned, flip the omelet again, and cook the other side for a minute.
3. Serve your amazing Chickpea Omelet topped with tomatoes, spinach, salsa, hot sauce, or whatever heart-safe, plant-perfect fixings you like.

Polenta with Pears and Cranberries

This polenta recipe is one of my favorites! For this recipe use the ripest pears you can find on the market—Bosc, Asian, or D'anjou—and fresh cranberries when they are in season (usually from October through December).

Ingredients

1/4 cup brown rice syrup

2 pears, peeled, cored, and diced

1 cup fresh or dried cranberries

1 teaspoon ground cinnamon

1 batch Basic Polenta, kept warm

Instructions

1. Heat the brown rice syrup in a medium saucepan. Add the pears, cranberries, and cinnamon and cook, stirring occasionally, until the pears are tender, about 10 minutes.
2. To serve, divide the polenta among 4 individual bowls and top with the pear compote.

FRUIT AND NUT OATMEAL

Oatmeal is one of my favorite breakfast foods. It is quick to prepare and easily adaptable to my ever-changing moods—some days I want it with fruit, some days I want it plain, and sometimes I want a little bit of everything in it (that's when I include all of the optional ingredients listed here!). This basic recipe is all you need to get started … add as much or as little of the extras as you like.

Ingredients

¾ cup rolled oats

¼ teaspoon ground cinnamon

Pinch of sea salt

¼ cup fresh berries (optional)

½ ripe banana, sliced (optional)

2 tablespoons chopped nuts, such as walnuts, pecans, or cashews (optional)

2 tablespoons dried fruit, such as raisins, cranberries, chopped apples, chopped

Apricots (optional)

Maple syrup (optional)

Instructions

1. Combine the oats and 1½ cups water in a small saucepan. Bring to a boil over high heat. Reduce the heat to medium-low and cook until the water has been absorbed, about 5 minutes.
2. Stir in the cinnamon and salt. Top with the berries, banana, nuts, and/or dried fruit, as you like. If desired, pour a little maple syrup on top. Serve hot.

EGYPTIAN BREAKFAST BEANS (FULMEDAMES)

This traditional Egyptian breakfast (pronounced fool mudammis) is almost always made with dried fava beans. They need to soak at least 8 hours before cooking, so start this dish the day before you want to serve it, to let the beans soak overnight. Ful Medames is usually served with pita bread and a fried egg, but take some liberty and serve it over brown rice with fresh lemon instead.

Ingredients

1½ pounds dried fava beans, soaked for 8 to 10 hours

1 medium yellow onion, peeled and diced small

4 cloves garlic, peeled and minced

1 teaspoon ground cumin

Zest and juice of 1 lemon

Sea salt

1 lemon, quartered

Instructions

1. Drain and rinse the beans and add them to a large pot. Cover with 4 inches of water and bring to a boil over high heat. Reduce the heat to medium, cover, and cook until the beans are tender, 1½ to 2 hours.
2. While the beans are cooking, sauté the onion in a medium skillet or saucepan over medium heat for 8 to 10 minutes, or until it is tender and starting to brown. Add the garlic, cumin, and lemon zest and juice and cook for 5 minutes longer. Set aside.
3. When the beans are fully cooked, drain all but ½ cup of the liquid from the pot and add the onion mixture to the beans. Mix well and season with salt to taste. Serve garnished with the lemon quarters.

APPLE-LEMON BREAKFAST BOWL

Fresh and deliciously filling, this apple-lemon breakfast bowl is beautifully flavored with dates, cinnamon, and walnuts.

Ingredients

4 to 5 medium apples, any variety

5 to 6 dates, pitted

Juice of 1 lemon (about 3 tablespoons)

2 tablespoons walnuts (about 6 walnut halves)

¼ teaspoon ground cinnamon

Instructions

1. Core the apples and cut into large pieces.
2. Place dates, half of the lemon juice, walnuts, cinnamon, and three quarters of the apple in the bowl of a food processor. Puree until finely ground, scraping down the sides of the bowl as needed.
3. Add the remainder of the apples and lemon juice and pulse until the apples are shredded and the date mixture is evenly distributed.

BREAKFAST SCRAMBLE

There are many very good recipes for scrambles, but most call for tofu. In this recipe, cauliflower takes the place of the tofu—with delicious results.

Ingredients

1 red onion, peeled and cut into ½-inch dice

1 red bell pepper, seeded and cut into ½-inch dice

1 green bell pepper, seeded and cut into ½-inch dice

2 cups sliced mushrooms (from about 8 ounces whole mushrooms)

1 large head cauliflower, cut into florets, or 2 (19-ounce) cans ackee, drained and gently rinsed

Sea salt

½ teaspoon freshly ground black pepper

1½ teaspoons turmeric

¼ teaspoon cayenne pepper, or to taste

3 cloves garlic, peeled and minced

1 to 2 tablespoons low-sodium soy sauce

¼ cup nutritional yeast (optional)

Instructions

Place the onion, red and green peppers, and mushrooms in a medium skillet or saucepan and sauté over medium-high heat for 7 to 8 minutes, or until the onion is translucent. Add water 1 to 2 tablespoons at a time to keep the vegetables from sticking to the pan.

Add the cauliflower and cook for 5 to 6 minutes, or until the florets are tender.

Add the salt to taste, pepper, turmeric, cayenne, garlic, soy sauce, and nutritional yeast (if using) to the pan, and cook for 5 minutes more, or until hot and fragrant.

BROWN RICE BREAKFAST PUDDING

My mom used to serve a version of this for breakfast—cooked with milk, sugar, and a hint of cinnamon. It is still one of my favorite breakfasts, although now I make a more wholesome version with almond milk and chopped dates.

Ingredients

3 cups cooked brown rice

2 cups unsweetened almond milk

1 cinnamon stick

⅛ to ¼ teaspoon ground cloves, to taste

1 cup dates, pitted and chopped

1 tart apple (such as Granny Smith), cored and chopped

¼ cup raisins

Salt to taste

¼ cup slivered almonds, toasted

Instructions

1. Combine the rice, almond milk, cinnamon stick, cloves, and dates in a medium saucepan and cook, stirring occasionally, over medium-low heat for 12 minutes, or until the mixture thickens.
2. Remove the cinnamon stick. Add the apple, raisins, and salt and mix.
3. Serve garnished with the toasted almonds

EASY OVERNIGHT OATS WITH CHIA

To get through those busy weeks, try this easy and healthy breakfast that you can make the night before.

Ingredients

¾ cup gluten-free rolled oats

¼ cup plant milk

½ cup water

1 heaping tablespoon chia seeds

½-1 tablespoon maple syrup

¼ teaspoon cinnamon

Dash of vanilla bean powder or extract

Fruit of choice

Instructions

1. Place oats, liquid, chia seeds, maple syrup, cinnamon, and vanilla into a 16-ounce mason jar or container of choice. Mix well. Seal shut and place jar in refrigerator overnight.

2. In the morning, mix again and top with anything you'd like, such as fresh fruit, more chia seeds, or cacao nibs.

WHOLE-WHEAT BERRY MUFFINS

These are a perfectly delicious breakfast muffin with loads of berry goodness and a tasty, wheaty backdrop. If you can find wild blueberries, use them—they are perfect for muffins because they're tiny and distribute beautifully without making the muffin soggy. If you use larger berries, like blackberries, slice them in half; otherwise they'll be too large. If you use frozen berries, bake the muffins for 26 minutes. If you use fresh, then 22 minutes should do it. Either way, check after 22 minutes to make sure you don't overbake.

Ingredients

⅔ cup unsweetened plant-based milk

1 tablespoon ground flaxseeds

1 teaspoon apple cider vinegar

2 cups whole-wheat pastry flour

2 teaspoons baking powder

¼ teaspoon baking soda

¾ teaspoon salt

½ cup unsweetened applesauce

½ cup pure maple syrup

1½ teaspoons pure vanilla extract

1 cup berries

Instructions

1. Preheat the oven to 350°F. Line a 12-cup muffin pan with silicone liners or use a nonstick or silicone muffin pan.
2. In a large measuring cup, use a fork to vigorously mix together the plant-based milk, flaxseeds, and vinegar. Mix for about a minute, until it appears foamy. Set aside.
3. In a medium mixing bowl, sift together the flour, baking powder, baking soda, and salt. Make a well in the center and pour in the milk mixture. Add the applesauce, maple syrup, and vanilla to the well and

stir together. Incorporate the dry ingredients into the wet ingredients until the dry ingredients are moistened (do not overmix). Fold in the berries.

4. Fill each muffin cup three-quarters full and bake for 22 to 26 minutes, or until a knife inserted through the center of a muffin comes out clean.

5. Let the muffins cool completely, about 20 minutes, then carefully run a knife around the edges of each muffin to remove them from the pan.

BLACK BEAN AND SWEET POTATO HASH

This black bean and sweet potato hash can be an ideal breakfast, a lunch, or a light dinner. It can be served simply as a side dish, spooned over brown rice or quinoa, wrapped in a whole-wheat tortilla, or made into soft tacos garnished with avocado, cilantro, and other favorite toppings. Make it in your Instant Pot or other pressure cooker, or do it the old-fashioned way, on the stovetop.

Ingredients

1 cup chopped onion

1 to 2 cloves garlic, minced

2 cups chopped peeled sweet potatoes (about 2 small or medium)

2 teaspoons mild or hot chili powder

⅓ cup low-sodium vegetable broth

1 cup cooked black beans

¼ cup chopped scallions

Splash of hot sauce (optional)

Chopped cilantro, for garnish

Instructions

Stovetop Method

1. Place the onions in a nonstick skillet and sauté over medium- heat, stirring occasionally, for 2 to 3 minutes. Add the garlic and stir.
2. Add the sweet potatoes and chili powder, and stir to coat the vegetables with the chili powder. Add broth and stir. Cook for about 12 minutes more, stirring occasionally, until the potatoes are cooked through. Add more liquid 1 to 2 tablespoons at a time as

needed, to keep the vegetables from sticking to the pan.

3. Add the black beans, scallions, and salt. Cook for 1 or 2 minutes more, until the beans are heated through.
4. Add the hot sauce (if using), and stir. Taste and adjust the seasonings. Top with chopped cilantro and serve.

Pressure Cooker Method

1. Heat a stovetop pressure cooker over medium heat or set an electric cooker to sauté. Add the onion and cook, stirring occasionally, for 2 to 3 minutes. Add the garlic and stir. Add the sweet potatoes and chili powder. Stir to coat the sweet potatoes with the chili powder. Add the broth and stir.
2. Lock the lid on the pressure cooker. Bring to high pressure for 3 minutes. Quick release the pressure. Remove the lid, tilting it away from you.

3. Add the black beans, scallions, and salt. Cook for 1 or 2 minutes more over medium heat, or lock on the lid for 3 minutes, until the beans are heated through.
4. Add the hot sauce (if using), and stir. Taste and adjust the seasonings. Top with chopped cilantro and serve.

CHOCOLATE PANCAKES

Everybody deserves to have a little chocolate for breakfast once in a while. These pancakes got five-star reviews from all of my testers. This recipe requires a nonstick skillet to keep the pancakes from sticking. Serve with whatever fresh fruit you like—we enjoy them with strawberries, raspberries, bananas, or a combination of all three.

Ingredients

1¼ cups whole-grain gluten-free flour (see Notes)

2 tablespoons unsweetened cocoa powder

1 tablespoon baking powder

1 tablespoon ground flaxseed

1 tablespoon vegan mini chocolate chips (optional; see Notes)

¼ teaspoon sea salt

1 cup unsweetened, unflavored almond milk

1 tablespoon pure maple syrup or ¼ teaspoon stevia powder

1 teaspoon vanilla extract

1 tablespoon apple cider vinegar

¼ cup unsweetened applesauce

Instructions

1. Combine the dry ingredients (flour, cocoa powder, baking powder, flax, chocolate chips, and salt) in a medium bowl. Whisk until fully combined.
2. Combine the wet ingredients (almond milk, maple syrup, vanilla, and vinegar) in a small bowl, and whisk well. This will create a vegan buttermilk for your pancakes.
3. Add the vegan buttermilk and the applesauce to the flour mixture, and stir until the batter is just combined.
4. Let the batter stand for 10 minutes while it rises and thickens as the flaxseeds soak; it may nearly double in size.
5. Heat a nonstick skillet or electric skillet griddle over medium heat and mist with a tiny bit of nonstick spray, if desired. (If you have a large skillet, you can cook multiple pancakes at once.) Scoop the batter into 3-inch rounds. Cook for 2 to 3 minutes or until the bubbles have burst in each of the pancakes and the tops start to appear dry. Flip the pancakes and cook for 1 to 2 minutes more. You should get 12 pancakes total.

Notes: Flour - You can use any other whole-grain flour if you prefer.

Chocolate chips - Two brands of vegan mini chocolate chips I like are Enjoy Life and Lily's (stevia-sweetened).

APPLE-WALNUT BREAKFAST BREAD

Slightly sweet, oil-free, and totally satisfying, this makes a great breakfast on the run. I know you want to eat it all in one sitting (I do, too), so to avoid that calorie splurge, cut it into single servings, wrap each in plastic wrap, and put them in the freezer until needed. This also makes a great baked gift. Wrap it up, tie it with a bow—now you're everyone's favorite breakfast baker!

Ingredients

1½ cups unsweetened applesauce

¾ cup packed light brown sugar

⅓ cup plain unsweetened almond milk or plant milk

1 tablespoon ground flax seeds mixed with 2 tablespoons warm water

2 cups all-purpose or whole wheat flour

1 teaspoon baking soda

½ teaspoon baking powder

1 teaspoon salt

1 teaspoon ground cinnamon

½ cup chopped walnuts

Instructions

1. Preheat the oven to 375°F.
2. In a large bowl, combine the applesauce, brown sugar, almond milk, and flax mixture and stir until smooth and well mixed. Set aside.
3. In a separate bowl, combine the flour, baking soda, baking powder, salt, and cinnamon. Mix the dry ingredients into the wet ingredients just until blended. Stir in the walnuts, then transfer the batter to a 9x5-inch loaf pan, spreading evenly and smoothing the top.
4. Bake until golden brown and a toothpick inserted in the center comes out clean, 25 to 30 minutes. Cool in the pan for about 20 minutes, then remove from the pan and cool completely on a wire rack.

CHAPTER EIGHT

LUNCH RECIPES

HOMEMADE VEGAN MOZZARELLA | CAPRESE SALAD

Have you ever thought about making your own plant-based mozzarella? Did you think you would have to give cheese for good after adopting a plant-based diet? I have great news for you! You can still have delicious vegan cheese and even venture into making your own! We have an amazing homemade vegan mozzarella recipe for you to try. Are you excited? We are too!

Cashew Love!

Making cheese is not something we aim to do every day, right? Well, with this delicious recipe, you might want to! The key ingredient for this homemade mozzarella to shine is cashews. These whitish nuts are front and center many creamy and "cheesy" plant-based dishes. You can use them to make "cheese sauce" or some scrumptious mac and cheese, and a huge array of raw desserts (among many other options!) Cashews are amazing!

The key is to soak them for long enough to develop their fantastic texture and release their super-rich flavor! So now you know, soak them, rinse them, process them!

An Italian Classic!

Caprese salad is an all-time Italian classic! Rich red tomatoes, bright green basil leaves, and creamy white mozzarella piled up together with a simple dressing. It's heaven! This crazy-simple recipe can be a side dish or an appetizer. If you decide to make it as an appetizer, you could serve it with some toasted baguette or sourdough bread drizzled with olive oil on the side.

Homemade Vegan Mozzarella: An All-rounder "cheese"!

Caprese salad is just one way to eat this incredible vegan mozzarella, but there are so many different plant-based creations you could add it to. Rustic vegan pizza with stringy mozzarella on top? Yes, please! A macaroni pasta bake topped with mozzarella? Yup! I highly encourage you to give it a try and experiment with it! It's so good you could even eat it with some salt and pepper.

Ingredients

For the mozzarella:

½ cup of raw cashews (soaked in water overnight)

1 tablespoon of freshly squeezed lemon juice

¼ teaspoon garlic powder

1 teaspoon nutritional yeast

1 teaspoon salt

½ cup of coconut oil

1 tablespoon agar agar powder

1 tablespoon of flour/tapioca starch

3 cups of water

For the salad:

3 roma tomatoes or regular large tomatoes (sliced)

2 handfuls of basil leaves (remove the steam)

Instruction

1. Place all the mozzarella ingredients in your blender or food processor. Blend or process until smooth
2. Pour the mix onto a dish (any shape will do) and let it sit in the fridge for about 6 to 7 hours at least (even better overnight!)
3. Remove from the dish and slice it as thick as you like.
4. On a dish assemble your salad. Place one slice of the mozzarella, then a slice of tomato on top and then a basil leaf. Continue doing this until you have a big enough portion (you also make it bigger and place it on a serving platter.
5. Choose your dressing of choice and drizzle on top. You can also just drizzle some olive oil and sprinkle some salt and pepper. Enjoy!

Butternut Squash Burrito

If you're scratching your head wondering about recipes and healthy eating for the new year, you're going to love this meal! With Cece's pre-cut veggie noodles, meal-prep time is cut in half. I just love how fresh and crispy they are and how easily they can blend into any recipe. These burritos are hearty and savory with a bit of butternut sweet. You'll be filled up with the good stuff and not left hungry. They're also great on the go.Enjoy

Ingredients

2 tablespoons of vegetable oil

1 small red onion, sliced

1 red or green bell pepper, sliced

3 large cloves of garlic, minced

1 package of Cece's Veggie Co Spiralized Butternut Squash Noodles

½ teaspoon cumin

2 flour burrito-size tortillas, warmed

1 (15-ounce) can of black or vegetarian refried beans

1 large avocado, pitted, peeled and sliced

Corn kernels (optional)

Cilantro (optional)

Salsa or hot sauce (optional)

Instruction

1. In a large pan over medium-high heat, heat the oil and saute the onion and bell pepper for 3 minutes. Add

garlic, butternut squash noodles, and cumin and saute for 3 minutes, or until all the veggies are tender.

2. Lay out your tortillas and add half of the butternut squash and veggie mixture to each tortilla.

3. Add a dollop of beans and avocado sliced to each tortilla, and add any other burrito fixings. Roll tightly into a burrito and enjoy!

TOFU & PESTO SANDWICH

This sandwich will absolutely blow your mind! It's simple and delicious and, most importantly, super filling. A triple win! Even if you're not a huge fan of tofu, you'll love this tofu pesto sandwich, it creamy and has so much flavor! Ready to dig in? Let's get to it!

Vegan Pesto On Everything!

Pesto is favorite wherever you go! It's so simple yet so delicious. Basil leaves pine nuts (or any other nuts you have) olive oil, garlic, salt, and pepper. That's it! Since pine nuts can be a bit pricey, you can find any nuts on sale and use them. I've tried them all, and they go so well. Walnuts, for example, are a great replacement! Make sure you choose the walnut slices because they are usually a lot cheaper than the whole walnuts. Another great choice is sunflower seeds; they are tasty and very nutritious. Do you have a favorite homemade green pesto recipe? Use it for this tofu pesto sandwich, and you'll love it even more!

Tofu Pesto Sandwich: The Perfect Lunch on The Go!

This sandwich is such an excellent option for lunch when we are in a hurry! Make it in the morning and take it with you in a paper bag (or silicon) and a glass container. It's super filling, nutritious, and uber tasty. Don't be surprised if your work colleagues (or college classmates) ask you for a bite or, even better, a recipe.

If you rather skip the bread, you could quickly turn this recipe into a tofu pesto salad or bowl. Cut the tofu into squares instead of slices and top with the pesto, then add shredded lettuce and chopped tomatoes to the mix. Voila! You have yourself another delicious lunch for the week! Pretty cool, right? Two lunches in one go!

Ingredients

4 tablespoons of green pesto (or any other pesto you like)

4 - 6 slices of tomato

2 - 4 butter lettuce leaves (or any lettuce you have on hand)

4 slices of sandwich bread (any will do)

A block of tofu sliced (thick enough to be able to roast it)

1 tablespoon of olive oil

dried oregano (to taste)

Instruction

1. Drizzle the tofu slices with the olive oil and sprinkle with the dried oregano.
2. Roast in a 375 F oven for about 15 minutes.
3. Once the tofu is done, assemble your sandwich. Spread one tablespoon of pesto on each slice of the sandwich, then place the lettuce, tomato, tofu. Enjoy!

ROASTED BRUSSEL SPROUTS WITH CRANBERRIES

Brussel sprouts have a really bad reputation, but that's just because people used to think that the only way to eat them was boiled. There is nothing attractive about soggy, brownish looking veggies, right? Well, I have great news! Roasting is the way to go, like these roasted Brussel's sprouts with cranberries recipe! This cooking method gives them a much brighter color and makes them taste divine!

Roasted Brussel Sprouts: The perfect Fall/Winter Side!

This recipe is such a great idea for a side dish! Eat them with some vegan pot pies or baked tofu, so delicious! It's especially great as a Thanksgiving or Christmas dinner recipe since it's main ingredients are so very seasonal. Would go perfect with lentil roast or vegan burgers, plus a gravy! Yum!

Ingredients

3 cups of brussel sprouts

2 tablespoons of olive oil

salt to taste

black pepper to taste

1/2 cup of dried cranberries

Instruction

1. Heat up the oven at 375 F.
2. Cut the brussels sprouts in halves and season them with the olive oil, salt, and pepper.
3. Place them on a baking tray and mix in the cranberries.
4. Cook them at 375 F for about 30 minutes. Serve and enjoy!

The Perfect Fall Salad

If we talk about quick, easy, and healthy meals, then salad should be at the top of the list! I'm not talking about those sad-looking iceberg lettuce with lemon salad but those nutrient-packed ones full of fiber and good fats! This fall salad is so delicious and filling you'll have it as main an aside.

Fall Flavors!

The flavors of this fall salad are so characteristic of this beautiful season! Pumpkin, walnuts, quinoa, pine nuts, and spinach! As with most of our recipes, you can add or replace anything you like. For example, pine nuts can be pricey, so just leave them out or buy them on sale.

Another great thing about this fall salad is that even though the flavors are very characteristic of the fall, you can prepare it year-round! Pretty awesome, right?

It's All About the Dressing!

Let's face it, you can have the best ingredients in a salad, but if the dressing is off, then the whole dish won't work out at all. The dressing is what coats all of the ingredients and brings out all of the flavors! In this case, it calls for a balsamic reduction. Still, you can use a super simple vinaigrette. Just put in a bowl, two tablespoons of the olive oil, one or two tablespoons of balsamic vinegar or lemon, salt, and a teaspoon of maple syrup. Wisk it all together until it thickens and voila! A perfect vinaigrette you can use for any recipe! If you're in a hurry, you can use a plant-based store-bought dressing also. So simple!

Add Some Protein!

If you're looking for some extra-protein, then you could pan-fry some cubes of tofu and top the salad with it. Super yummy! What about roasting some chickpeas and then throwing them in there? So many great options!

Ingredients

2 cups of baby spinach

1 cup of cooked pumpkin

¼ of an onion

¼ of a cup of cooked quinoa

1 teaspoon of pine nuts

⅙ cup of walnuts

1/2 tablespoon of balsamic reduction

salt to taste

pepper to taste

Instruction

Assemble the salad, season and enjoy!

MUSHROOM STUFFING

It's that time of the year again where we get to see our loved ones and get to be thankful for all we have. But it's also the time to focus on ALL the yummy food this holiday brings. Let's face it, Thanksgiving food is so delicious and comforting we kind of look forward to this day all year long. It's also a great chance to choose healthier plant-based options and get busy in the kitchen, re-creating all of our favorite childhood dishes. One of those is stuffing, and we love it! Let's dive into this vegan mushroom recipe!

Easy to Find Ingredients!

This vegan mushroom stuffing is creamy and crazy delicious! It only uses super easy to find winter veggies like celery, carrots, mushrooms, and onions. If we had to pick the one thing that makes stuffing a stuffing is the bread! The bread is so essential to this recipe because it absorbs all the juices coming out fo the veggies and just brings everything together.

Which Bread is Best?

When it comes to stuffing the older, the better, any bread you have leftover for days and seems stale and dry would be so perfect for this recipe. Any kind will do — cornbread, sourdough, or rustic. You can try with the different ones and see which one you like best.

Yummy Mushrooms!

Mushrooms are so perfect for a recipe like this! They have a meaty flavor, and they have so much water content that make any recipe extra juicy after it's been cooked. They are also super light and budget-friendly! This recipe uses classic white mushrooms, but you could try and replace them for another kind, like Portobello or oyster mushrooms.

What do you say? Are you inspired to try this mushroom stuffing recipe this Thanksgiving? Try to include a few plant-based dishes this holiday and explore the fantastic world of vegan food!

Ingredients

1 loaf of bread, cubed

1 clove of garlic, diced

1 red onion, sliced

1 medium carrot, diced

1 rib of celery, diced

1 cup of mushrooms, sliced

2 cups of vegetable stock

fresh thyme

2 tablespoons of vegetable oil

Instruction

1. Roast the bread in a baking tray, for about 15 minutes - it should become gold and crispy.
2. Meanwhile in a hot pan with some oil, start cooking the onions, garlic, celery, and carrots.
3. After 2 minutes you can add in the mushrooms and season with fresh thyme, salt, and pepper.
4. et that cook for another 5 minutes and now add in the vegetable stock. Let it simmer for 2 minutes and take off the heat.
5. ransfer to the tray with the bread, but make sure that all the liquid has been absorbed - that will assure that the bread won't become soggy. Serve and enjoy!

GREEN BEAN CASSEROLE

For the past 13 years, I've been hosting an annual vegan Friendsgiving potluck the weekend after Thanksgiving. It's a way for my friends to try new recipes, gather, and share a plant-based nourishing-to-the-body-and-soul meal together.

This year, the recipe that I've been trying to perfect for our potluck is the Green Bean Casserole. I wanted it to be a combination of down-right-tasty, but also a recipe that doesn't require hours in the kitchen. This is what I came up with!

I did all my shopping at Sprouts, they had everything I needed, including the fried onions– which I thought I was going to have to make from scratch. I used the Sprouts organic frozen green beans as the center of this dish so that I could remove a step of having to cook them myself.

Ingredients

2 cups of water

2 vegetable bouillon cubes

3 ½ tablespoons of vegetable or canola oil

½ cup of yellow onion, diced

1 ½ cups of cremini mushrooms, diced

3 cloves of garlic, minced

3 ½ tablespoons of all-purpose flour

½ teaspoon of dried oregano

1 bag of frozen green beans

1 (6-ounce) package of fried onions

Instruction

1) Preheat oven to 400 degrees F.
2) In a microwave-safe bowl, microwave the water and bouillon cubes until cubes are completely dissolved. Stir and set aside.
3) Heat the oil in a saucepan over medium heat, then add the onions, mushrooms, and garlic. Saute until onions for about 3 to 4 minutes or until they are translucent and tender.
4) Add the flour and mix to form a thick paste. Allow to cook, stirring, 1-2 minutes until golden.
5) Add the bouillon broth, stir, and bring to a simmer over medium heat. Season with dried oregano and ground pepper.
6) Use a whisk to gently mix the gravy until it thickens to your desired consistency (about 15 minutes).
7) Stir in 1 bag of frozen green beans.
8) Transfer to a large cast-iron skillet and top with fried onions.
9) Bake for 15 minutes. Remove from heat and serve warm.

CHAPTER NINE

DINNER RECIPES

Italian Cannellini Bean Stew with Mustard Greens & Parmesan

Ingredients

1 onion

2 garlic cloves

1 carrot

1 celery stalk

4 oz mustard greens

1 lemon

13.4 oz cannellini beans

2 vegan Italian sausages

1 tsp herbs de Provence

4 tsp vegetable broth concentrate

1 tbsp soy-free vegan parmesan

1 tbsp + 1 tsp olive oil*

Instructions

Prepare the vegetables

Peel and chop the onion. Peel and mince the garlic. Peel and chop the carrots into rounds. Slice the celery. Cut tough stems off the mustard greens and chop the leaves. Halve the lemon and cut one half into wedges. Drain and rinse the beans.

Crisp the sausage

Remove sausages from the packaging and slice into rounds. Place a large pot over medium-high heat with 1 tbsp olive oil. Once hot, add the sliced sausage and cook until browned, tossing occasionally, about 3 to 5 minutes. Transfer crispy sausage to a plate and cover to keep warm.

Begin the stew

Return the pot to medium-high heat with 1 tsp olive oil. Add the chopped onion, minced garlic, chopped carrot, and sliced celery and cook, until softened, about 3 to 5 minutes. Add the beans, herbs de Provence, vegetable broth concentrate, and 2 cups water and stir to combine. Bring the stew to a boil and reduce heat to medium. Simmer until vegetables are tender, about 4 to 6 minutes.

Add the greens

Add the chopped mustard greens to the pot and simmer until vegetables are just tender, another 3 to 5 minutes. Remove the pot from heat, squeeze the juice from half of the lemon into the pot, and drop the lemon in. Season the stew with ½ tsp salt and a pinch of pepper.

Serve

Ladle the Italian cannellini stew into large bowls. Top with crispy sausage and sprinkle with parmesan. Serve with lemon wedges. Buon appetito!

BANHMI SANDWICHES WITH TERIYAKI TOFU & QUICK PICKLED VEGETABLES

Ingredients

1 cucumber

1 jalapeño

2 carrots

7 oz Wildwood Organic SprouTofu Baked Teriyaki Tofu

¼ oz fresh cilantro

¼ oz fresh mint

¼ cup apple cider vinegar

1 tsp turbinado sugar

2 ciabatta bread

3 tbsp Follow Your Heart Soy-Free Vegenaise

1 tbsp Roland Sriracha

Instructions

Prepare the vegetables

Thinly slice the cucumber on the bias. Thinly slice the jalapeño. Peel the carrots and grate using the largest side of a box grater. Slice the tofu lengthwise into 6 steaks. Pick the cilantro leaves and mint leaves from the stems.

Pickle the vegetables

Add the apple cider vinegar, sugar, and ½ cup water to a small saucepan. Bring to a boil and remove from heat. Add the sliced cucumber and sliced jalapeño to a medium bowl, cover with the pickling liquid, and transfer to the refrigerator to cool.

Crisp the tofu

Place a large skillet over medium-high heat with 1 tbsp vegetable oil. Once the oil is hot, add the sliced tofu and cook until crispy in places, about 3 to 5 minutes per side.

Make the Sriracha mayo

Set the oven to broil on high. Halve the ciabatta bread and place directly on the oven rack. Bake until warm, about 2 to 3 minutes. Add the Vegenaise and Sriracha to a small bowl and mix the Sriacha mayo well.

Serve

Layer the teriyaki tofu, quick pickled vegetables, grated carrot, cilantro leaves, and mint leaves onto the toasted ciabatta and top with Sririacha mayo. Enjoy!

TROPICAL GRAIN BOWL WITH PAN-SEARED AVOCADO & MANGO VINAIGRETTE

Ingredients

½ cup bulgur wheat

1 mango

2 garlic cloves

½ oz fresh cilantro

1 tbsp white vinegar

2 tsp agave

6 oz lacinato kale

1 avocado

2 oz shredded red cabbage

2 tbsp pumpkin seeds

2 tbsp pecans

4 tbsp olive oil*

Instructions

Cook the wheat berries

Add ⅔ cup (1 ⅓ cup) water to a small saucepan and bring to a boil. Add the bulgur, cover, and remove from heat. Allow the bulgur to rest until last instruction.

Make the mango vinaigrette

Peel the mango, remove the flesh from the pit, and dice. Peel and mince the garlic. Chop the cilantro leaves and stems. In large bowl, combine the diced mango, minced garlic, chopped cilantro, white vinegar, agave, and a pinch of salt and pepper. While whisking, drizzle in 2 tbsp (4 tbsp) olive oil. Taste and adjust the seasoning of the mango vinaigrette with salt.

Prepare the kale

Destem the kale and thinly slice the leaves. Add the sliced kale to the bowl with the mango vinaigrette and toss to coat.

Sear the avocados

Halve the avocado and remove the pit. Sprinkle each half with a pinch of salt. Place a large nonstick skillet over medium-high heat with 2 tbsp olive oil. Once hot, add both avocado halves, cut-side down. Cook, undisturbed, until well browned, about 3 to 4 minutes.

Serve

Divide the cooked bulgur wheat between large, shallow bowls. Top with marinated kale, cabbage, pumpkin seeds, and pecans. Scoop out the pan-seared avocados and place on top of the bowls. Drizzle with any remaining mango vinaigrette. Enjoy!

CAULIFLOWER SHAWARMA WITH HARISSA BEET SLAW & GARLIC AIOLI

Ingredients

6 oz cauliflower florets

1 Roma tomato

1 shallot

2 tsp baharat spice blend

2 garlic cloves

3 tbsp Follow Your Heart Soy Free Vegenaise

1 lemon

1 tbsp harissa paste

1 tbsp tahini

2 oz shredded red beets

4 oz Arcadian Harvest Classic greens

2 multigrain flatbreads

2 tsp vegetable oil

1 tbsp olive oil

Salt and pepper

Instructions

Prepare the vegetables

Preheat oven to 400°F. Chop the cauliflower florets into bite-size pieces. Thinly slice the tomato into half moons. Peel and thinly slice the shallot.

Roast the cauliflower

Transfer the cauliflower florets to a baking sheet and toss with 1 tbsp vegetable oil, baharat spice, and a pinch of salt and pepper until evenly coated. Roast until tender and browned in places, about 12 to 15 minutes.

Make the aioli and slaw

Peel and mince the garlic and add to a small bowl. Add Vegenaise and a pinch of salt. Mix garlic aioli well to combine. Halve the lemon. In a medium bowl combine just 2 tsp lemon juice, harissa paste, tahini, and 1 tsp water until well combined. Add beets to the bowl and toss until harissa beet slaw is evenly coated.

Make the salad

In a large bowl, add the greens, remaining lemon juice, 1 tbsp olive oil, and a pinch of salt and pepper. Gently toss the salad. Place the flatbreads in the oven to warm for 1 minute.

Serve

Spread the garlic aioli on the flatbreads. Top each flatbread with cauliflower shawarma, sliced tomato, sliced shallot, harissa beet slaw, and ¼ cup salad. Fold the flatbreads to make sandwiches and serve with the remaining salad. Dig in!

TAMARIND CAULIFLOWER WITH GINGERED FRIED RICE & CASHEWS

Ingredients

8 oz cauliflower florets

3 garlic cloves

1 oz fresh ginger

2 bird's eye chile

1 Roma tomato

2 scallions

4 oz green beans

8 oz precooked brown rice

1 tbsp gluten free tamari

¼ cup cashews

¼ cup tamarind sauce

2 tbsp vegetable oil

Salt

Instructions

Roast the cauliflower

Preheat the oven to 425°F. Add the cauliflower florets to a baking sheet and coat with 2 tsp (4 tsp) vegetable oil. Season with a pinch of salt and roast until tender and browned in places, about 15 to 20 minutes.

Prepare the vegetables

Peel and mince the garlic and ginger. Cut the tomato into wedges. Chop the scallions into 2 inch pieces. Chop the green beans into ½ inch pieces. Mince the bird's eye chiles.

Cook the vegetables

Place a large nonstick skillet over medium-high heat with 1 tbsp vegetable oil. Once hot, add just half of the minced garlic and just half of the minced ginger. Cook, stirring constantly, until garlic is just toasted, about 1 to 2 minutes. Add the tomato wedges, chopped scallions, and green beans, and cook until vegetables are tender, about 1 to 2 minutes.

Add the rice

Add the brown rice to the skillet and cook until slightly toasted and heated through, about 2 to 3 minutes. Stir in the tamari and cook for 1 more minute. Taste and adjust the seasoning with salt if necessary. Divide the gingered fried rice between large serving plates.

Prepare the tamarind sauce

Return the skillet to medium-high heat, with 1 tsp vegetable oil and the cashews. Cook until toasted, about 2 to 4 minutes; then add the remaining minced garlic, ginger, and as much minced chile as you'd like. Cook, stirring constantly, until fragrant, about 1 minute. Add the tamarind sauce, reduce heat to medium, and simmer until slightly thickened, less than 1 minute.

Serve

Add the roasted cauliflower to the skillet. Cook, tossing often, until cauliflower is well coated and sticky, about 1 to 2 minutes. Top the gingered fried rice with tamarind cauliflower. Enjoy!

CAJUN BAKED TOFU WITH CREAMED SWISS CHARD & PICKLED CAULIFLOWER

Ingredients

15.5 oz Nasoya Organic Extra Firm Tofu

1 tbsp Cajun seasoning

1 shallot

2 garlic cloves

8 oz Swiss chard

5.5 oz coconut milk

2 tbsp nutritional yeast

2 oz curried pickled cauliflower

1 tbsp + 2 tsp vegetable or coconut oil

Salt and pepper

Instructions

Bake the tofu

Preheat the oven to 425°F. Drain the tofu and pat dry with paper towels. Cut into 1 inch cubes and transfer to a baking sheet. Toss tofu with Cajun seasoning and 1 tbsp (2 tbsp) vegetable oil, and bake until crisp in places, about 20 to 25 minutes.

Prepare the produce

Peel and thinly slice the shallot. Peel and mince the garlic. Roughly chop the Swiss chard leaves and stems.

Sauté the chard

Place a medium saucepan over medium heat with 2 tsp (4 tsp) vegetable oil. Once hot, add the sliced shallot, minced garlic, ¼ tsp (½ tsp) salt, and ¼ tsp (½ tsp) pepper and cook until softened, about 3 to 4 minutes. Add the chopped Swiss chard and cook until just wilted, about 2 to 3 minutes.

Cream the Swiss chard

Add the coconut milk and nutritional yeast to the sautéed chard and stir to combine. Reduce the heat to low and simmer until the creamed Swiss chard is slightly thickened, about 4 to 5 minutes.

Serve

Divide the creamed Swiss chard between plates and top with Cajun baked tofu. Serve with the curried pickled cauliflower. Dig in!

CHICKPEA PASTA WITH CRISPY ARTICHOKE HEARTS & CHARRED PEPPER RAGOUT

Ingredients

5 garlic cloves

1 red bell pepper

1 yellow bell pepper

1 jalapeño pepper

4 oz grape tomatoes

8 oz Banza rotini

13.75 oz artichoke hearts

1 tbsp vegan parmesan

1 tbsp + 2 tsp vegetable oil*

Salt and pepper*

Instructions

Prepare the vegetables

Bring a large pot of salted water to boil. Peel the garlic. Trim and deseed the red and yellow bell peppers, and chop into large pieces. Deseed and roughly chop the jalapeño.

Char the vegetables

Set the oven to broil on high. Add the garlic, chopped peppers, as much chopped jalapeño as you'd like, and the grape tomatoes to a baking sheet. Drizzle with 2 tsp (4 tsp) vegetable oil and sprinkle with ½ tsp (1 tsp) salt and ¼ tsp (½ tsp) pepper. Broil on the middle rack until the peppers are charred, about 8 to 10 minutes.

Cook the pasta

Add the rotini to the boiling water and stir. Cook until al dente, about 6 to 8 minutes. Reserve ½ cup (1 cup) of the pasta water and drain the pasta. Rinse with cool water to stop the cooking process.

Blend the ragout

Add the charred vegetables and ¼ tsp (½ tsp) salt to a food processor and pulse until evenly chopped, about 3 to 5 pulses.

Broil the artichoke hearts

Drain the artichoke hearts, pat dry, and add to the baking sheet. Toss with 1 tbsp (2 tbsp) vegetable oil and a pinch of salt and pepper, and broil on the middle rack until crispy, about 6 to 8 minutes.

Serve

Return the large pot to medium heat and add the charred pepper ragout. Once it's simmering, add the pasta, reserved pasta water, and just 2 tsp (4 tsp) of parmesan. Cook, stirring frequently, until heated through, about 3 to 4 minutes. Divide the chickpea pasta between large shallow bowls. Top with crispy artichoke hearts and remaining parmesan. Enjoy!

CHAPTER TEN

ENTREES(STARTERS) RECIPES

CHOCOLATE PEANUT BUTTER SHAKE

Dessert for breakfast? Yes, please. This dairy-free Chocolate Peanut Butter Shake makes a great dessert, but an even better plant-based breakfast. It's rich, creamy, savory and sweet!

Taste aside; it's filled with fiber, antioxidants, natural plant-protein, and potassium! All the fuel you will need to power through your day. If dessert for breakfast isn't enough to make someone go plant-based, I don't know what is.

Ingredients:

2 frozen bananas

3 Tablespoons raw cacao powder

3Tablespoons natural peanut butter

1 cup almond milk/soy milk (suggested: West Soy)

Cacao is a raw, ground cocoa bean. You can find it in the baking section of your grocery store.

Instructions:

1. Combine ingredients in a blender, and process until smooth
2. Enjoy!

EASY PLANT-BASED SOUPS FOR THE BLENDER

Looking for an easy way to stay on track with your whole food plant-based diet? Keep it simple, sweetie -- and make blender soups! These two recipes can be chilled or heated up for hearty, delicious, and above all else, easy meals.

Carrot Orange Soup

It's full of vitamin C, antioxidants, and flavor!

Servings: 2

Ingredients:

1 lb. carrots, chopped

½ navel orange

½ red bell pepper

1 celery stalk

1/2 cloves garlic

1 tsp. freshly chopped ginger

½ tsp lime juice

pinch of salt

2 ½ cups of water

½ cup of cashews (optional)

Instructions:

Put all ingredients in a high-speed blender and mix until smooth.

Blender Beet Soup

Next up, a beet soup that blends to a beautiful red-purple color. According to Dr. Caldwell Esselstyn, beets have a big serving of antioxidants - a key factor in heart health.

Servings: 2

Ingredients:

2 bunches of beets

½ - 1 cup of orange juice

zest of one lemon

2 -3 tablespoons of lemon juice

6 mint leaves

pepper, to taste

Instructions:

Boil beets 40 minutes or more, depending on their size, until just tender. Peel. Whirl in food processor (or high speed blender) with juices, zest, mint and pepper. Chill. Serve with mint leaf on top.

PORTOBELLO PLANT-BASED "BLT" SANDWICH

The holidays can get busy, so it's nice to have a quick lunch recipe in your back pocket when you're up to your elbows in wrapping paper and holiday planning. Let's face it; sometimes it's difficult to choose between bacon and good health...this healthy version of a not-so-healthy favorite will help make that decision a little easier. Introducing: a plant-based BLT...or more accurately, PLT - Portobello Lettuce and Tomato.

Keep in mind that avocado really completed this plant-based BLT - subbing in as a great replacement for mayo!

Ingredients:

- 1 Portobello mushroom cap

- 2 TBS of water

- 2 TBS of Tamari

- ½ an avocado

- ½ a lemon

- A few pieces of lettuce

- 2 slices of tomato

- dash of garlic powder

- dash of crushed black pepper

- 2 slices of whole grain (or GF) bread, toasted

Instructions:

1. Preheat your oven to 350

2. Slice your Portobello mushroom cap into thin slices and arrange on a non-stick baking pan and spritz with a few TBS of water
3. Bake for 15 minutes (until juices begin to run)
4. Brush with a few TBS of Tamari and bake for an additional 5 minutes
5. Spread the avocado onto both slices of toast and add the lettuce and tomato
6. Squirt with lemon and sprinkle with black pepper and garlic powder
7. Finally, add the roasted mushrooms and enjoy!

EASY VEGAN ALFREDO SAUCE WITH BROCCOLI AND PASTA

Time for you to rejoice because vegan alfredo sauce is a real thing.

This easy vegan alfredo sauce recipe includes whole food plant based pasta and broccoli. It's a healthy spin on your not so healthy favorite and makes the perfect quick and nutritious weeknight vegan pasta dish. You'll love it. It's cholesterol free, low fat, and packed with protein and iron.

Ingredients

1 small head of broccoli, chopped

2 cloves of garlic, crushed

1/2 a cup of veggie broth, low sodium

1 cup of vegan alfredo sauce

⅓ pound of dry pasta

black pepper

Instructions

1. Add to boiling water ⅓ of a pound of dry whole food plant-based pasta of choice and cook until al dente (check pasta package for specific cook times)
2. While pasta's cooking, de-stem, and chop broccoli into small pieces
3. Then saute until soft (about 10 minutes)... Broccoli pieces and veggie broth
4. Now add... Crushed garlic and cook for 5 more minutes
5. Finally... Mix cooked pasta together garlic, broccoli, and Mac Sauce.
6. Finish with... Black pepper to taste. This tastes great garnished with fresh chopped basil or oregano.

Homemade Cashew Cream Sauce

Soak covered in water...

2 cups raw cashews

Add to the bowl of a food processor and blend with...

zest and juice and of 1 lemon

2 Tablespoons nutritional yeast

fresh ground pepper to taste

pinch of sea salt to taste

Happy Noshing!

FUDGY VEGAN BROWNIE RECIPE

Black beans in brownies? You bet your plant-based bottom! Turns out, they're actually what's been missing from your vegan brownie recipe all along. Black beans make the ideal fudgy brownie dough. And this recipe is gluten-free, refined sugar-free, and high in fiber, protein, and potassium. All good reasons to have another brownie.

Ingredients:

2 cups cooked sweet potato

1 cup black beans

8 dates, soaked and pitted

6 Tablespoons cocoa powder

6 Tablespoons natural peanut butter

¼ cup of maple or date syrup

¼ cup of coconut flakes or crushed walnuts (optional)

Instruction

Preheat oven to 350 while you blend until smooth...

Sweet potato

Black Beans

Dates

Cocoa powder

Natural peanut butter

Maple or date syrup

Then...

Spread into a baking sheet and top with coconut flakes or walnuts

Bake for 25-30 minutes

Chill for a few hours and enjoy cold!

Happy Noshing!

CHAPTER ELEVEN

SMOOTHIES AND BEVERAGE RECIPES

CREAMY DRAGON FRUIT SMOOTHIE BOWL

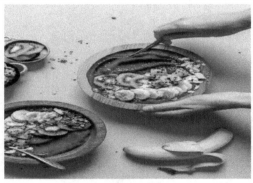

Sometimes your food just needs to be extra. Like, you don't just want it to taste good. You also want it to look beautiful.

Those two needs are happily met in this SUPER creamy Dragon Fruit Smoothie Bowl that's ready in 5 minutes with just 5 wholesome ingredients.

Frozen banana creates the creamy, sweet base. Frozen raspberries (or other berry of choice) add a bit of fruit flavor and antioxidants, while frozen dragon fruit creates that gorgeous hot-pink hue.

To be honest, dragon fruit doesn't taste like much (but it adds tons of health-promoting vitamins and minerals), which is why adding any combination of fruit and protein powder will affect the flavor however you wish!

Frozen banana creates the creamy, sweet base. Frozen raspberries (or other berry of choice) add a bit of fruit flavor and antioxidants, while frozen dragon fruit creates that gorgeous hot-pink hue.

The secret to a thick smoothie bowl consistency?

Blend slow and slow

Scrape often

Add only as much liquid as needed to blend

It's as easy as that!

Ingredients

SMOOTHIE BOWLS

- 2 packets frozen dragon fruit* (unsweetened // we like PitayaPlus brand)
- 1/2 cup frozen raspberries (or other fruit of choice)
- 2 medium ripe bananas previously peeled, sliced, and frozen
- 3 Tbsp Vegan Vanilla Protein Powder (right now, we like Nuzest and Tropeaka)
- 1/4 - 1/2 cup dairy-free milk (we used DIY Coconut Milk)

TOPPINGS optional

- Coconut flakes
- Fresh fruit
- Hemp seeds
- Granola

Instructions

1. To a high-speed blender, add frozen dragon fruit, frozen raspberries, banana, protein powder, and dairy-free milk (starting with lower end of range). Blend until creamy and smooth. The trick to a thick smoothie bowl is being patient and blending slowly, adding only as much liquid as necessary, and using a smoothie wand (or something comparable that's blender safe) to scrape the sides down as it blends.
2. Taste and adjust flavor as needed, adding more banana for sweetness, dairy-free milk for creaminess, or berries for more intense berry flavor.
3. Divide between serving bowls and enjoy as is or top with fruit fruit, granola, hemp seeds, and coconut flakes (optional).
4. Best when fresh. Store leftovers in the refrigerator up to 24 hours. Freeze for longer-term storage. Or freeze in ice cube mold to use in future smoothies.

Notes

2 packets dragonfruit equals approximately 3/4 cup dragonfruit.

1 scoop Vegan Vanilla Protein Powder equals approximately 12g.

Nutrition information is a rough estimate calculated with coconut milk, Nuzest vanilla protein powder, and without toppings.

SUPER GREEN SMOOTHIE BOWL

There's a certain sense of accomplishment that comes with working out and getting in two servings each of fruit and vegetables before 10 a.m. But have you heard the new thing about smoothies? You can put them in BOWLS. Yes, bowls. Why, you ask?

Because you can make them into even more of a complete meal with the simple addition of a few blend-in ingredients and toppings. Count me in!

This smoothie bowl is absolutely delicious. Plus, it's simple (as always), requiring just 10 minutes to make, and entirely customizable. I provide a basic round-up of ingredients for you to start with so you can then experiment and make this bowl your own.

The basic idea, in my opinion, is to make a slightly thicker, more nutritionally dense smoothie (with things like avocado and nut butter) and then top it with some game-changing ingredients, like coconut, hemp seeds, granola, nut butters, etc. You get the drift.

Basically, anything in your pantry that will take your smoothie from tide-me-over snack to seriously-substantial meal.

My ideal green smoothie bowl has:

Super bright green color (achieved with lighter-colored berries and loads of greens)

Nut butter for extra protein

Avocado for healthy fats and richness

Flaxseed meal for fiber

And natural sweetness from frozen bananas

Ingredients

SMOOTHIE

1. 1/4 ripe avocado
2. 2 medium ripe bananas (previously sliced and frozen)
3. 1 cup fresh or frozen mixed berries (organic when possible // use strawberries/raspberries for a greener smoothie, darker berries for a purple smoothie)
4. 2 large handfuls spinach (organic when possible)
5. 1 small handful kale (organic when possible // large stems removed)
6. 1 1/2 - 2 cups unsweetened non-dairy milk (DIY or store-bought - will depend on if your berries are frozen)
7. 1 Tbsp flaxseed meal

8. 2 Tbsp salted creamy almond or peanut butter (optional)
9. TOPPINGS (optional)
10. Roasted unsalted sunflower seeds
11. Granola
12. Raw or roasted nuts (almonds, pecans, walnuts, etc.)
13. Shredded unsweetened coconut
14. Fresh berries
15. Hemp seeds
16.

Instructions

1. Add all smoothie ingredients to a blender and blend until creamy and smooth. Add more almond milk (or water) to thin.
2. Taste and adjust flavor as needed, adding more ripe banana (or maple syrup) for added sweetness, more spinach for a bright green hue, or almond milk for creaminess.
3. For the green smoothie, I used strawberries, which let the green color come through more. For the purple bowl, I used darker berries (raspberries, blackberries, blueberries).
4. For more protein, add nut butter! This also offsets / enhances the natural sweetness of the smoothie.
5. Divide between 2 serving bowls (as original recipe is written // adjust if altering batch size) and top with desired toppings!
6. Best when fresh, though leftovers can be kept in jars in the fridge for up to 1-2 days.

Notes

Nutrition information is a rough estimate calculated with nut butter and without toppings.

CREAMY GOLDEN MILK SMOOTHIE

If you're into golden milk, this smoothie is a must-try! It requires 7 wholesome ingredients (you likely have on hand right now), 1 blender, and 5 minutes to make. Let's do this!

The base of this smoothie is frozen banana for natural sweetness and a creamy texture. We tested other fruits and nothing quite worked. But if you're trying (or prefer) to avoid banana, we include another option in the notes!

For anti-inflammatory, antioxidant, and digestion benefits, we included plenty of fresh ginger and ground turmeric. Black pepper boosts the absorption of turmeric, so we added that as well. And don't forget cinnamon for more natural sweetness and warmth.

Coconut milk keeps things super creamy, and as an optional touch, we threw in some fresh carrot juice to balance the banana flavor and provide an even more intense orange (golden) hue.

Ingredients

SMOOTHIE

- 1 cup banana* (ripe, sliced, and frozen)
- 1 cup light coconut milk or almond milk (or store-bought // use full-fat coconut for creamier smoothie)
- 1/2 tsp ground turmeric (preferred flavor over fresh)
- 1 Tbsp fresh ginger (plus more to taste)
- 1 Dash ground cinnamon
- 1 Dash black pepper
- 1 Dash ground nutmeg
- 1 Dash ground clove and cardamom (optional // for more warmth + spice)
- 1/4 cup fresh carrot juice* (optional // for color, added sweetness + balances banana flavor // or sub 1 small carrot!)
-

FOR SERVING optional

1 Tbsp Hemp seeds

Instructions

1. Add banana, coconut milk, turmeric, ginger, cinnamon, black pepper, and nutmeg to a high-speed blender and blend on high until creamy and smooth. If including, add cardamom, clove, and fresh carrot juice at this time (optional).

2. If too thick, thin with more coconut milk or water. If too thin, thicken with ice (or more frozen banana, though it will add more sweetness).

3. Taste and adjust flavor as needed, adding more cinnamon for warmth, black pepper for spice, ginger for "zing," turmeric for earthiness / more intense color, or banana for sweetness. Adding carrot juice will also add sweetness and more intense orange/yellow hue.

4. Divide between serving glasses (ours are from West Elm) and enjoy immediately. Keep leftovers in the refrigerator for 24 hours. Freeze leftovers by pouring into an ice cube tray and use for future smoothies (either this smoothie or others you'd like to infuse with a golden milk flavor).

CREAMY GOLDEN MILK SMOOTHIE

Our Vegan Golden Milk Smoothie served in two glasses with straws. If you're into golden milk, this smoothie is a must-try! It requires 7 wholesome ingredients (you likely have on hand right now), 1 blender, and 5 minutes to make. Let's do this!

Banana, turmeric, ginger, carrots, coconut milk, and warming spices for making our Vegan Golden Milk Smoothie

The base of this smoothie is frozen banana for natural sweetness and a creamy texture. We tested other fruits and nothing quite worked. But if you're trying (or prefer) to avoid banana, we include another option in the notes!

For anti-inflammatory, antioxidant, and digestion benefits, we included plenty of fresh ginger and ground turmeric.

Black pepper boosts the absorption of turmeric, so we added that as well. And don't forget cinnamon for more natural sweetness and warmth.

Coconut milk keeps things super creamy, and as an optional touch, we threw in some fresh carrot juice to balance the banana flavor and provide an even more intense orange (golden) hue.

Ingredients in a blender for making our plant-based Golden Milk Smoothie Pouring our vibrantly-colored Vegan Golden Milk Smoothie into a serving glass

This would make the perfect quick breakfast or snack. For a little extra protein, add in some hemp seeds or protein powder of choice. And for the real deal, check out our 5-Minute Vegan Golden Milk!

Want more healthy smoothie ideas? Check out our Carrot Ginger Turmeric Smoothie, Super Green Spirulina Smoothie, Almond Butter Blueberry Smoothie, and Creamy Zucchini Blueberry Smoothie.

CREAMY GOLDEN MILK SMOOTHIE

All of the delicious taste and health perks of golden milk in smoothie form! Just 7 ingredients, 1 blender, and 5 minutes required. Creamy, naturally sweet, subtly spiced, and packed with turmeric!

Ingredients

- 1 cup banana* (ripe, sliced, and frozen)
- 1 cup light coconut milk or almond milk (or store-bought // use full-fat coconut for creamier smoothie)
- 1/2 tsp ground turmeric (preferred flavor over fresh)
- 1 Tbsp fresh ginger (plus more to taste)
- 1 Dash ground cinnamon
- 1 Dash black pepper
- 1 Dash ground nutmeg
- 1 Dash ground clove and cardamom (optional // for more warmth + spice)
- 1/4 cup fresh carrot juice* (optional // for color, added sweetness + balances banana flavor // or sub 1 small carrot!)
-

FOR SERVING optional

1 Tbsp Hemp seeds

Instructions

1. Add banana, coconut milk, turmeric, ginger, cinnamon, black pepper, and nutmeg to a high-speed blender and blend on high until creamy and smooth. If including, add cardamom, clove, and fresh carrot juice at this time (optional).
2. If too thick, thin with more coconut milk or water. If too thin, thicken with ice (or more frozen banana, though it will add more sweetness).
3. Taste and adjust flavor as needed, adding more cinnamon for warmth, black pepper for spice, ginger for "zing," turmeric for earthiness / more intense color, or banana for sweetness. Adding carrot juice

will also add sweetness and more intense orange/yellow hue.

4. Divide between serving glasses (ours are from West Elm) and enjoy immediately. Keep leftovers in the refrigerator for 24 hours. Freeze leftovers by pouring into an ice cube tray and use for future smoothies (either this smoothie or others you'd like to infuse with a golden milk flavor).

Notes

If you're trying to avoid/sub banana, we'd recommend using the recommended amount of carrot juice, swap the banana for the same amount of cauliflower, and add some vanilla protein powder for sweetness.

Make carrot juice in a juicer, buy at the store, or add 1 raw or cooked carrot to the smoothie to a similar effect.

Nutrition information is a rough estimate based on full recipe calculated with light (canned) coconut milk and without optional ingredients.

CREAMY AVOCADO BANANA GREEN SMOOTHIE

Whenever we travel, the one thing I'm usually able to find, wherever we go, is a smoothie.

Thankfully, they seem to be readily available and a great way to get in some vegetables and fruit, which helps me feel a bit more "in my routine" even when I'm not. This creamy avocado smoothie was inspired by a recent trip to Iceland, where I hit the smoothie jackpot. Let me show you how it's made!

This creamy avocado smoothie is easy to make, requiring just 5 ingredients, 1 blender, and 5 minutes.

The base is frozen banana, which creates a creamy, naturally sweet base. Next comes the star ingredient: avocado! Full of fiber and healthy fats, avocado makes this smoothie creamy and dreamy and thick, almost like a milkshake.

Ingredients

SMOOTHIE

- 1 large frozen banana (ripe // peeled // sliced)
- 1/4 – 1/2 medium ripe avocado (more avocado = creamier, thicker smoothie)
- 1 scoop plain or vanilla protein powder
- 1 large handful greens of choice (spinach, kale, rainbow chard // I like mine frozen)
- 3/4 – 1 cup unsweetened plain almond milk (or any dairy-free milk)

ADD-INS optional

- 1 Tbsp seed of choice (hemp, flax, sesame, sunflower, chia, etc.)
- 1/2 tsp adaptogen of choice (maca, ashwagandha, etc.)
- 1/2 cup sliced frozen (or fresh) cucumber or berries (organic when possible)

Instructions

1. To a high-speed blender, add frozen banana, avocado, protein powder of choice, greens, and dairy-free milk. At this time, add any desired add-ins, such as adaptogens, seeds, or additional fruits and vegetables (such as berries or cucumbers).
2. Blend on high until creamy and smooth, scraping down sides as needed. If smoothie is too thick, add more dairy-free milk to thin. If too thin, add more frozen banana or avocado.
3. Taste and adjust flavor as needed, adding more banana for sweetness, avocado for creaminess, or

greens for vibrant green color. Protein powder can also be used to add more sweetness (depending on brand / flavor).

4. Divide between serving glasses and enjoy! Best when fresh, though leftovers will keep covered in the refrigerator up to 24 hours or in the freezer up to 2 weeks.

Notes

Nutrition information is a rough estimate calculated with vegan protein powder and without additional add-ins.

IMMUNE BOOSTER ORANGE SMOOTHIE

This smoothie also contains cinnamon, ginger and turmeric, all of which act as anti-inflammatory agents in the body, among many other benefits.

This combination also adds a warm, spicy undertone that complements the sweetness of the sweet potato perfectly.

Last but not least, orange juice adds plenty of Vitamin C and extra immune-boosting benefits to hep ward off any stubborn colds this winter.

Ingredients

- 1 cup loosely packed sweet potato puree (1 large potato yields ~ 1 cup or 328 g // skin removed // or sub pumpkin puree + extra banana or maple syrup for sweetness)
- 1 medium ripe banana (previously sliced and frozen)
- 1 Tbsp almond butter (optional)
- 1/4 tsp each ground turmeric, cinnamon, and ginger (if using fresh ginger, use 1 tsp chopped per 1/4 tsp dried)
- 1/2 Tbsp flaxseed meal or chia seeds
- 3/4 cup unsweetened almond milk
- 1/4 cup orange juice (optional)
- 1 large handful ice

Instructions

1. To bake your sweet potato, preheat oven to 400 degrees F (204 C) and split in half lengthwise. Lightly oil and place face down on a foil-lined baking sheet. Bake until soft - 25-30 minutes.
2. Or, to steam, place in a steamer basket over 2 inches of simmering water and cover to steam for roughly 5-10 minutes or until fork tender. Let cool slightly before adding to blender.
3. Add all ingredients to a blender and blend until smooth, scraping down sides as needed.

4. Taste and adjust seasonings/sweetness as needed. Add more banana or orange for added sweetness, and more ice to thicken.

5. Split between two small glasses (as original recipe is written // adjust if altering batch size) and serve. Garnish with extra cinnamon.

Notes

Nutrition information is a rough estimate calculated without optional ingredients.

CHAPTER TWELVE

DESSERT RECIPES

SEA SALT BUTTERSCOTCH TART

Ingredients

SHORTBREAD CRUST

- ½ cup granulated sugar
- ¼ cup virgin coconut oil, at room temperature, or softened butter
- 1 teaspoon pure vanilla extract
- 2 cups almond meal flour
- ½ teaspoon salt

FILLING

- ⅔ cup packed light brown sugar or coconut sugar
- ⅔ cup canned coconut cream
- ½ cup coconut oil or butter

- 1 teaspoon kosher salt
- Flaked sea salt, as needed
- 1 Granny Smith apple, sliced (optional)

Instruction

1. Preheat the oven to 375°F and have a 9-inch round tart pan or a 4-by-14-inch tart pan nearby.
2. MAKE THE CRUST: In a bowl with a handheld mixer or a stand mixer with a paddle attachment, mix the granulated sugar, coconut oil and vanilla together until fluffy. Mix in the almond meal flour and salt. Then press the mixture evenly into the bottom and up the sides of the tart pan.
3. Place the entire tart pan in the freezer for 10 minutes to harden, then bake in the oven until the edge is brown and the center is crusty, 15 minutes. Remove from the oven and let cool.
4. MAKE THE FILLING: In a saucepan, combine the brown sugar, coconut cream, coconut oil and salt. Bring to a boil and then cook over medium heat for about 25 minutes. Have a cup of ice water nearby. Dip the tip of a fork into the boiling sugar and then into the ice water; if the sugar sticks between the tines of the fork without dissolving, the filling is ready. Pour it into the cooled tart crust, sprinklewith sea salt, arrange the apple slices on top, if desired, and let it cool and harden before slicing and serving.

STRAWBERRY-MANGO HAWAIIAN SHAVE ICE

It's impossible to visit Hawaii without eating a towering mountain of rainbow shave ice. This summer, the trend has crossed the Pacific and swept through the rest of the country. See the DIY version be, strawberry-mango Hawaiian shave ice—no shave ice machine necessary.

Ingredients

- 4 servings
- 1 cup sugar, preferably superfine, divided
- 1 quart strawberries, diced
- 1½ cups mango juice
- 1 mango, diced
- ½ cup toasted coconut

Instructions

1. In a medium pot, bring 1 cup water and ¾ cup of the sugar to a boil over medium heat. Once the mixture

has boiled, remove from the heat and add 2 cups water.

2. Pour the mixture into a shallow baking dish and transfer to the freezer for 5 hours, stirring the mixture every 45 minutes to create ice crystals.

3. In a blender, process the strawberries and the remaining ¼ cup sugar until smooth. Strain the mixture and transfer to a container with a pour spout. Transfer the mango juice to a container with a pour spout.

4. To serve, divide the ice into four serving glasses. Pour about a quarter of the mango juice over each, then pour about a quarter of the strawberry mixture over each as well. Garnish with mango and coconut.

BEST VEGAN SNICKERDOODLES

Ingredients

- 2 1/2 cups (350g) spelt, white whole wheat or all-purpose flour
- 2 teaspoons cream of tarter
- 1 teaspoon baking soda
- generous pinch of mineral salt

- 1 cup (225g) vegan butter, at room temp (I love Miyokos)
- 1 cup (225g) organic pure cane sugar
- 1/4 cup (56g) unsweetened applesauce (see notes)
- 2 teaspoons vanilla extract

For rolling:

- 3 tablespoons organic pure cane sugar
- 1 tablespoon cinnamon

Instructions

1. Preheat oven to 375 degrees F. Line a baking sheet with silpat or parchment paper, or lightly grease with oil.
2. In a mixing bowl, combine the flour, cream of tarter, baking soda and salt. Set aside.
3. In a medium sized mixing bowl, using a spoon, mix together the sugar and butter until creamy, about 2 minutes. This can also be done with a stand alone mixer or hand blender (I usually just use a bowl and spoon). Then add the vanilla and applesauce, mix to combine. Add flour mixture and stir just until flour is incorporated. Dough should be firm and thick. If the dough is too soft, chill it in the refrigerator for 15 minutes to 1 hour until it stiffens a bit. This will help keep them from spreading too much.
4. In a small bowl, combine the sugar and cinnamon for rolling. Roll dough into about 1 inch balls. To keep them uniform, use either a 1 tablespoon measuring spoon or 1 tablespoon scooper.

5. Place cinnamon sugar rolled balls on prepared baking sheet, leaving about 2 inches between balls. Bake in center of the oven for 8 – 9 minutes. For a little crispier cookie, bake for 10 minutes.

6. Let cool for a few minutes on the pan, they may be too soft just from the oven to move to a wire rack. Once cooled, enjoy!

7. Makes about 28 cookies

8. Store cookies covered on the counter for up to 3 days. Keep them fresher longer by storing them in the refrigerator for up 10 days. Freeze leftovers for up to 2 months (let thaw before eating).

NOTES:

If you don't have cream of tarter on hand, or prefer to make snickerdoodles without it, you can easily substitute the cream of tartar AND the baking soda with 2 teaspoons of baking powder.

In place of applesauce, feel free to use a flax egg (1 heaping tablespoon flaxseed meal + 3 tablespoons water, let set for 10 min.) or use 1/4 cup of your favorite unsweetened non-dairy milk

CHAPTER THIRTEEN

SAUCES, DRESSINGS AND DIPS

FAUX CHEESE SAUCE

Faux Cheese Sauce (Gluten-Free and Vegan)

Ingredients

1/4 c Nutritional Yeast

2 Tbsp rice flour* (wheat flour can be used instead)

1/4 tsp tumeric

1/2 tsp onion powder

1/2 tsp garlic powder

salt to taste (I used 1/2 tsp)

1/4 tsp cumin**

1/2 tsp chili powder**

1 c plant milk (I use rice or unsweetened almond milk)

For a thicker sauce add extra flour. These are optional but best used for a Mexican inspired flavor.

Instructions

1. In a medium sauce pan add all dry ingredients and place on medium heat.
2. Stir with a wisk as dry ingredients are heated and begin to toast. Don't let them burn!
3. Once they are warmed and begin to be very fragrant (again, not burnt) add the plant milk and wisk often.
4. Once sauce becomes thick remove from heat and let cool for a few minutes.
5. Serve

I like this drizzled over potatoes, broccoli, mixed into a casserole, or best yet on nachos. Unlike other recipes I've tried this one stays pretty fluid and is versatile enough to use in a number of different recipes.

RASPBERRY VINAIGRETTE SALAD DRESSING

Oil-Free Raspberry Vinaigrette Salad Dressing

Ingredients

1 heaping cup of fresh raspberries, if you need to use frozen allow them to thaw first

1/2 cup of water

up to a 1/2 tsp of red wine vinegar

2 Tbsp maple syrup (more or less to taste)

a dash of salt and pepper

Instructions

1. Pour your raspberries, half of the water, half of the vinegar and maple syrup into a blender. I used my Blendtec. Add your salt and pepper.
2. Press the pulse button and allow to process until everything liquefies. Pour in slightly more water if needed.

3. Give your dressing a taste test. Add more vinegar and maple syrup if needed. Some berries are sweeter while others are sour so this isn't an exact science. I made it as written above and it was perfect for us.
4. If you adjusted your ingredients pulse again until your salad dressing reaches the right consistency and flavor.

Your salad dressing will be a beautiful raspberry color and taste slightly sweet with just enough kick.

This will make about 1 1/2 cups depending on how much water you use. Store this dressing in the refrigerator and use within 5 days.

CREAMY CRANBERRY SALSA DIP (DAIRY FREE)

If you like things on the spicy side, you can leave the ribs and seeds of the jalapeño in or add a second one. For my palate, and my kids, one with seeds and ribs removed, is just right.

This salsa has a lot of the same components of traditional salsa, but of course with cranberries instead of tomatoes.

s

Ingredients

Cranberry Salsa

12 oz bag fresh cranberries (rinsed and drained)

2 small or 1 large jalapeño (or to taste)

1/2 cup diced red onion

1/4 cup chopped cilantro

1/3 cup coconut sugar

2 tbsp maple syrup

1/2 tsp salt

juice of 1 lime

Cashew Cream Cheese

1 1/2 cups raw cashews (soaked for several hours)

1 tbsp apple cider vinegar

2 tbsp lemon juice

1 tsp salt

1-2 tbsp water (if needed)

Instructions

1. Place all ingredients for cranberry salsa in a food processor and pulse until combined. Don't over process or you will end up with a puree. You want it to be slightly chunky still.

2. Pour into a medium bowl and refrigerate.

3. Place all ingredients for the cashew cream cheese, except the water, into the food processor (just rinse it out after the salsa). Puree until smooth. Add the 1-2 tbsp of water, if needed, to thin it out.

4. Mix the cranberry salsa with the cashew cream cheese until combined.

5. Refrigerate at least 30 minutes or until serving.

CHAPTER FOURTEEN

SNACKS RECIPES

KALE BRUSCHETTA

We adore this as an appetizer, and so does everyone else. It is always the first empty platter at our holiday party. No one knows it is plant-based; they just know it is so yummy.

Ingredients

1 bunch kale

1 loaf fresh 100% whole-grain bread, sliced

½ cup Cannellini Bean Sauce

1 cup grape tomatoes, halved

balsamic glaze

Instructions

1. Place the kale leaves in a large pot of boiling water. Cover and cook until tender, about 5 minutes. Drain in a colander, then squeeze out any extra liquid with your hands (you don't want soggy bread).
2. Toast 8 pieces of bread, and place them on a handsome serving platter.
3. Spread a tablespoon of the Cannellini Bean Sauce on the toasted bread, then cover with a layer of kale and top with a scattering of grape tomatoes. Drizzle generously with the balsamic glaze, and grab one for yourself before they all disappear.

CARAMELIZED ONION & PEPPER VEGAN QUESADILLAS

Catering for Whole Foods Market was one of the best jobs I've ever had. Not only was it a great company to work for, but also I was able to enjoy mouth-watering dishes. One of my favorites was their vegan quesadillas—the inspiration for this savory recipe. With a creamy plant-based cheese, a little spice and fresh greens, these vegan quesadillas have flavor and texture that I think is even more delicious than traditional quesadillas!

Ingredients

¾ cup raw cashews, soaked for 2 hours

½ cup nutritional yeast flakes

1 lime, juiced

½ tablespoon stoneground mustard, no-salt added

½ cup water

1 yellow onion, sliced thin

1 red bell pepper, sliced thin

1 yellow bell pepper, sliced thin

1½ tablespoons ground cumin

1½ teaspoon chili powder

8 100% corn tortillas, no salt or oil added

2 cups fresh spinach, loosely packed

Instructions

1. Make the cheese sauce: Add the cashews, nutritional yeast, lime, stoneground mustard and water to a blender. Blend until it the sauce is creamy. Set it aside.
2. Make the onion-pepper filling: Place a sauté pan over medium heat. Add the sliced onion and bell pepper. Stir in the cumin and chili powder. Cover and cook for

5 minutes, stirring occasionally so the veggies don't stick to the bottom of the pan. Then stir in a tablespoon of water and continue cooking uncovered. When the water evaporates stir in another tablespoon of water, continuing to sauté until the onions are caramelized.

3. Turn the heat to low. Pour the cheese sauce into the onion and peppers. Stir well and then cover with a lid so the mixture doesn't dry out.

4. Make the first quesadilla: Place a non-stick pan over medium heat. Let it heat for 5 minutes. Then place one of the tortillas into the pan. Set a timer, letting the first side toast for 2 minutes and then flip. Set the timer for another 2 minutes. As you wait, carefully scoop about ¼ of the filling onto the tortilla and spread it evenly, forming a single layer of peppers and onions. Layer ½ cup of spinach across the onions and peppers. Place the second tortilla on top of the spinach.

5. Once the timer goes off or the bottom side is toasted, use a large spatula to carefully flip the entire quesadilla. Toast the second tortilla for 2-3 minutes.

6. When the quesadilla is done transfer it to a plate. Repeat this process with the remaining filling to make a total of 4 quesadillas. Note that subsequent quesadillas may require less cooking time because the pan will be hotter. You may want to turn the heat down slightly after the first couple. Slice the quesadillas into triangular pieces and serve.

Note: Soaking the cashews softens them so they become creamy when blended. If you're using a high-powered blender such as a vitamix, the nuts do not need to be soaked.

ORANGE BLACK BEAN TAQUITOS

The orange zest and juice in this recipe brighten the dish and elevate the ordinary black bean to new heights. Serve this with cooked brown rice or quinoa and a salad. These taquitos are also great for hearty snacking.

Ingredients

1 large yellow onion, diced small

4 cloves garlic, minced

2 teaspoons cumin seeds, toasted and ground

2 chiles in adobo sauce, minced, or 2 teaspoons ancho chile powder

Zest and juice of 2 oranges

2 (15-ounce) cans black beans, drained and rinsed (about 3 cups)

Sea salt

18 corn tortillas

1½ cups Spiked Sour Cream

1 jar salsa

Instructions

1. Sauté the onions in a saucepan over medium heat for 8 to 10 minutes. Add water 1 to 2 tablespoons at a time, to keep them from sticking. Add the garlic and cook for another minute. Add the cumin, chiles in adobo sauce, orange zest and juice, and black beans.
2. Season with salt to taste, and purée the mixture in a food processor until smooth but still a little chunky.
3. Place the tortillas, a few at a time, in a nonstick skillet over medium-low heat. Heat until softened, 3 to 4 minutes. Stack the warmed tortillas and wrap them in a piece of foil.
4. Spread 3 tablespoons of the black bean mixture over half of each tortilla, then roll up the tortilla and set it aside. Repeat with the remaining tortillas, then place all of the taquitos into a large nonstick skillet and heat over medium-low heat for 3 to 4 minutes.
5. Serve with the Spiked Sour Cream and salsa.

CONCLUSION

Identifying specific foods (or components of them) that can increase the risk of, or even cause, certain diseases, is notoriously difficult. There are many problems associated with trying to tease out the links between diet and disease. For example, most diet and breast cancer risk studies have been conducted in industrialised countries (North America, Europe and Japan). Comparing the diets between industrialised and developing countries rather than within them could offer more insight as the diets between these countries tend to vary more. This may permit a better comparison, for example, of a plant-based diet versus an animal food-based diet or a soya versus non-soya diet.

Another problem is that self-reported diets (food diaries and food frequency questionnaires) are often assessed with considerable measurement error. Furthermore, most studies tend to focus on the diet consumed as an adult, whereas strong evidence suggests dietary influences before adulthood can affect breast cancer risk later in life. For example, research shows that a high soya intake during adolescence can reduce the risk of breast cancer later in life. The average follow-up time may be too short to determine significant conclusions. The effect of diet on different sub-types of cancer such as: oestrogen receptor-positive, progesterone receptor-positive, genetic (due to faulty genes), epigenetic (not due to genes) warrants further investigation. For example, salad vegetables have been shown to lower the risk of HER-2 positive breast cancer. The positive effect of some foods may be masked by the negative effects of others. For example, in the Shanghai Study the authors suggest that the potential positive effect of vegetables and soya foods may have been countered by the negative effects of fish in the diet.

Furthermore, the effects of specific diets (such as macrobiotic, organic, wholefood, raw food or vegan) have not been sufficiently studied.

The supposed health benefits of meat and dairy foods have been vigorously promoted by the meat and dairy industries for decades. For example, the idea that meat is essential for iron and protein is deep-rooted and is often used to pressure would-be veggies back to the butchers. The reality is that we do not need saturated animal fat, animal protein or cholesterol. We do not need the trans fatty acids in processed foods. We do not need the amount of salt and sugar we consume. We do however need to move towards a plant-based, wholegrain diet containing a wide range of fruits, vegetables, grains, pulses, nuts and seeds for the nutrients that will promote a long and healthy life.

These, of course, are the same foods which contain protection against disease in the form of antioxidants and fibre. What is killing the Western world are the degenerative diseases associated with affluence. It is clear that the same diet that is good for preventing breast cancer is also good for preventing heart disease, obesity, diabetes and so on.

The milk debate deserves a special mention here as the notion that cow's milk is a natural and healthy drink for humans is so deeply entrenched in the British psyche, yet the evidence suggests milk may be doing us more harm than good. Of course we need calcium for our bones and teeth

(and blood clotting, muscle function and regulating heart rhythm). But despite the dairy industry's powerful marketing machine, more and more people are beginning to wonder if cow's milk really is the best source of calcium. It certainly is not for most of the world's people. Claims that dairy is best carry strong overtones of cultural imperialism and simply ignore the 70 per cent of the global population who obtain their calcium from other sources - people such as the Japanese who traditionally have consumed no dairy yet have far better health than British people and live considerably longer.

Milk has been part of the human diet for less than 6,000 years; this is very recent in evolutionary terms. It is not just that most people don't drink it; they cannot because their bodies will not tolerate it. Up to 100 per cent of some ethnic groups are lactose intolerant. In global terms lactose intolerance is very common, occurring in around 90-100 per cent of Asians, 65-70 per cent of Africans, but just 10 per cent of Caucasians (Robbins, 2001). This suggests that the health claims made for milk owe more to marketing than science.

The dairy industry has spent many years and many millions of pounds promoting the notion that cow's milk is good for us through expensive advertising campaigns such as the 'White Stuff'. Now, because of an increasing body of evidence, there are signs of a growing realisation that milk is neither natural nor healthy. In fact, research is moving in the opposite direction now, showing that the more dairy and animal protein that is consumed, the higher the incidence of osteoporosis and other diseases.

The rate at which some cancers are increasing is a huge matter of concern. When Professor Jane Plant wrote the first edition of Your Life in Your Hands in 2000, one in 10 UK women were affected by the disease. Now, in 2007, one in nine women are expected to develop breast cancer at some point in their lives! Since 1971, the incidence of breast cancer in the UK has increased by 80 per cent. These figures should be shouted from the rooftops! An increasing number of researchers are in no doubt that cow's milk and dairy foods are responsible.

The official approach to the causes of breast cancer (and other so-called diseases of affluence) remains extremely equivocal and dietary advice seems to be based far more on not upsetting particular vested interests than improving the public's health. As a consequence, the incidence of these diseases continues to rise remorselessly because public health policy is aimed, almost exclusively, at treatment rather than prevention.

Only when prevention becomes the priority will the avoidance of animal products be seen as central to improving public health. The World Health Organisation believes that the only way we can improve our health is through informed opinion and active co-operation. We agree! As a science-based health charity, Plant Based provides unbiased information on which people can make informed choices. We monitor and interpret scientific research on diet and health communicate those findings to the public, health professionals, schools and food manufacturers. Importantly, we have no commercial or vested interests and offer a vital - and what sometimes feels like a solitary - source of accurate and unbiased information.

So it is up to individual members of the public and independent-minded health professionals to find out what they can about diet and health.